"Let's liven up the party!"

Curtis flipped a long, thick, ropelike object toward Frank. It landed half on and half off him. It was a big rattler, and its mouth opened so wide with fury that Frank could have put his entire fist into it. He rolled with terrified speed, dumping the snake before its deadly fangs touched him.

Charlie stepped forward and flipped the rattler toward Singer. "It's for you," he shouted. "It's a girl snake."

Singer ducked, but he wasn't fast enough. The rattler fell across his shoulder and with writhing fury wrapped itself around his neck.

The sharp, poisonous fang struck home and the vicious horseplay had turned into tragedy and death.

Another Gold Medal Original by

Clair Huffaker:

GUNS OF RIO CONCHOS

COWBOY

A Gold Medal Novel by

Clair Huffaker

Adapted from the screenplay by Edmund H. North
and *Reminiscences of a Cowboy* by Frank Harris

GOLD MEDAL BOOKS

FAWCETT PUBLICATIONS, INC.
President, W. H. Fawcett, Jr.
Secretary-Treasurer, Gordon Fawcett
FAWCETT BLDG., FAWCETT PLACE, GREENWICH, CONN.

Cowboy

CHAPTER ONE

Reece is on his way!"

"Holy jumpin' Jesus, Reece is comin'!"

The slender, immaculate young man behind the hotel desk glanced up from the letters he was sorting. The second of the two men who had spoken in loud, excited voices was hurrying past his desk.

"My dear sir!" the young man said sharply. The man wheeled to a halt, his eyes impatient and questioning.

"Please remember where you are," the desk clerk said. "This is hardly the place for such language."

"What the hell, son! Didn't you hear who's comin'? Tom Reece!"

"And just who is Mr. Reece?" the clerk asked, stiffening at the second curse word that came to his ears.

"The cowman!" The other man whirled abruptly, as though he'd spent too much time explaining a thing that anyone in his right mind already knew. He walked swiftly away from the desk through the lobby that was now milling with excited people.

Fascinated against his will at the magic the name had produced in the hotel, the stiff-backed desk clerk stared over the mahogany counter, unconsciously fingering the nameplate on the desk in front of him that said in unobtrusive letters, "Mr. Frank Harris."

The large, ornate lobby was rapidly filling with men who scurried back and forth over the thick rugs between the elaborately scrolled columns, or stood in buzzing conversations near the large potted plants placed about the room.

From behind the desk the office door opened and the hotel manager, an erect, impeccable, gray-haired man of fifty stepped to the desk. "What seems to be the trouble, Mr. Harris? We have a certain dignity to uphold here."

"I can't understand it, sir. Some cowboy is on his way, and—"

"Cowboy?" The manager sounded offended. "The Royal Hotel hardly caters to cowboys."

Harris shrugged. "As I say, I don't understand it. Some cowboy named Reece—"

"Reece! Oh, my God!" The manager's voice went up an octave. "He's in early this year! And as for you, Harris, Mr. Reece is not a cowboy! He's a cowman! There's a world of difference!"

"But I—"

"No time for chatter!" the manager snapped. "Smith! Tucker! Hamblin!"

The three waiting bellboys came to the desk, and the bell captain, sensing the urgency in the manager's voice, hurried over to join them. "What is it, Mr. Fowler?"

"Mr. Reece is on his way." Fowler spoke rapidly now, like an officer giving crucial orders to his men. "Smith. Get every available person to work getting Mr. Reece's trunks out of storage! See to it that every piece of clothing is freshly pressed! Start with the evening clothes. You, Hamblin, run to the kitchen and alert the chef and wine steward! They'll know what to do! But remind the chef he'll need extra waiters!

"Tucker, get up to the second floor and see to it there's plenty of hot water. And tell Johnson to make sure the ballroom is ready for a large, formal party later this evening! You stay here, Captain, to greet Mr. Reece as he comes in. I'll join you in a moment."

As the others hurried away, Harris turned to Fowler and said, "We didn't make this much fuss over the Governor."

"The Governor is not Mr. Reece!" Fowler hesitated. "You seem slightly dazed, Harris."

"I am."

"Well, don't be! Mr. Reece insists upon efficiency!" Fowler put his fingers to his forehead in thought. "Now, let's see. Mr. Reece will want the entire south wing of the second floor, at least."

"But we have guests occupying part of that wing. The Vidals."

"Yes. They'll have to be moved, of course."

"Mr. Fowler! You can't move people like the Vidals! They're aristocrats!"

But Fowler ignored his horrified protests. A husky Spaniard, dressed in dirty, rough clothes, was walking toward the desk. To Harris's shock, Fowler leaned across the desk and extended his arm to shake hands. "Good to see you, Mr. Mendoza! Welcome back. And how is Mr. Reece?"

"He's fine. He sent me ahead to tell you he was coming."

"Ahh, we already know. He'll want his usual accommodations?"

"That's right. Just like always." Mendoza's keen, dark eyes swept from Fowler to Harris. "The south wing, and half a dozen spare rooms close by, just in case."

"Some of those rooms are occupied," Harris said firmly.

"Harris!" Fowler's voice cracked with authority. He turned to Mendoza, and his smile asked forgiveness. "The youngster is new here. Everything will be ready for Mr. Reece."

The Spaniard nodded and recrossed the lobby, and Fowler turned to the younger man. "You've had some rapport with the Señorita Vidal, I believe."

"We've exchanged a few words."

"Good. Since you'll be on familiar ground, you can move them."

"But, sir—"

Fowler rushed away before Harris could finish. Frowning, the young man straightened his cravat, then drummed his fingers on the desk as he stared reflectively at a gas lamp flickering from a nearby wall. After a long moment, he signaled for the bell captain to watch the desk for him, and started toward the second floor.

At Room 206, Harris raised a hand to knock, but then dropped it soundlessly. How could you tell people like the Vidals—like Maria—that they are being thrown out of their rooms because some odd character who hires tough-looking Mexicans is coming to the hotel?

The door swung open suddenly, and Maria looked out. "Oh," she said in a low voice. "I thought I heard someone. I thought it was Father." She stepped out into the corridor, gently shutting the door behind her. "You know I can't see you here, Frank."

Looking at the soft black hair that framed her white face, and the large, luminous eyes that were now studying him with affection, Frank found himself wordless. "I—" Taking one of her hands in both of his, he whispered, "Darling, it's not you I've come to see. I have to talk to your father."

"My father? Do you think that's wise?"

"No." Harris blushed quickly and was furious at himself for it. "I know it's too early to say anything about us. It's something altogether different. It's—it's about these rooms. Something has come up."

"What has come up, Frank?"

"Well—" Frank took a deep breath. "You see, they're

having trouble with the plumbing on the third floor. There's a lot of water all over the place above you, and it will be leaking down pretty soon. So for your own convenience, and all, it will be better for you if we move you into some more comfortable rooms. There's a nice suite available on the third floor." Hesitating, he said, "You see what I mean. Will it be all right if I come in and wait for your father, so I can explain to him?"

Maria leaned forward suddenly and kissed him swiftly on the cheek. "Yes, of course. Do come in. But try not to let him see how it is between us. In my country, we do not do things the way you do here."

Grinning self-consciously, Frank said, "I'll try to treat you as a hotel guest instead of a sweetheart."

Inside the large, lavish room, Maria gestured him to an overstuffed chair with a floral design on it. Smiling from across the room, she told him, "I like that word. Sweetheart. It is a very pretty word."

"Speaking of pretty words—" Frank struggled to say what he wanted said. "Did you like the poem I sent you?"

"The poem?"

"Yes. I didn't just copy it, Maria. I wrote it myself. It took me about six hours."

"But I didn't get any poem."

They both turned as the door opened, and Señor Vidal came into the room. A fine-featured, haughty Spanish gentleman, his eyebrows lifted slightly as he saw Frank sitting in the room.

Standing, Frank said, "I was waiting for you, sir. I have to talk to you about your rooms."

"Not about my daughter?"

His cheeks coloring once more, Frank wet his lips nervously. "Your rooms."

"Did you write this poem to my rooms?" Señor Vidal took a small piece of paper from his pocket.

"No, sir. I wrote it to your daughter."

"I thought so. Your taste in women is excellent. Your artistry as a poet leaves much to be desired."

His jaw tightening, Frank said, "Good or bad, I wouldn't have written it if I thought her mail would be opened."

Señor Vidal's eyes became hard, and Maria moved toward him. "What Mr. Harris has done is quite acceptable in America, Father."

Wadding the paper into a ball, Vidal crossed the room and threw it into a wastebasket by the desk. "We will, of course, be leaving your hotel immediately. I can't tolerate a romance between you, Maria, and—a hotel clerk."

"I won't be a hotel clerk all my life!" Frank's hands became fists. "Chicago's just a jumping-off spot for me. I'm going to become a cattleman. Right now I'm just waiting for the right man to go in with!"

"Money is not everything, regardless of the attitude in Chicago." Vidal went to the door and opened it. "Will you be so good as to have our bill sent up?"

Facing Maria, Frank said in a low voice, "Will you wait for me? I'll come for you."

Glancing uncertainly at her father, Maria dropped her eyes. "I'll try, Frank," she whispered. "That's all I can promise."

As the younger man moved toward the door, Vidal said flatly, "Give up, Mr. Harris. There are some things in life that are denied to each of us."

His stomach tight with anger, Frank descended the stairs and took his position behind the desk.

A few minutes later there was a fusillade of roaring shots from out on the street, mixed with wild yells of sheer delight.

Offbaugh, the house detective, hurried out of the office behind the desk. "That'll be Reece."

"You going to make him stop shooting?"

"Lord, no! I'm going to square things with the patrolmen on duty!" Offbaugh started around the desk.

"I guess Reece could commit murder and get away with it," Frank grumbled.

A heavy, sober man, Offbaugh considered the question with brief seriousness. "No doubt about it, in my mind." Then he hurried across the lobby, beyond where Fowler and the bell captain were waiting with wide, fixed smiles on their faces.

CHAPTER TWO

T HE HOTEL LOBBY seemed to tremble under the impact as Reece and his men strode quickly in through the wide doors. There was no way to mistake Reece. He was the spearhead of the rugged little army strung out behind him. Tall, with powerful lines to his jaw and face, he was wide-shouldered and flat-stomached. Moving with controlled strength and grace toward the desk, he favored Fowler and the bell captain with the briefest nod as they hurried to intercept him. A worn bedroll was thrown over one shoulder, and he was dressed in dirty levis and work shirt. His high-heeled boots were dusty and old, and a curly-brimmed black Stetson was as much a part of him as the dark hair that showed under it in short, crisp waves. Half a dozen men whom Frank recognized as big Chicago cattle buyers were strung out behind him, mingling with a crowd of tough-looking cowboys with hard, clear eyes, who were dressed much like their boss.

Frank turned the registration book toward Reece as the man and his party surrounded the desk. Reece glanced at him briefly and Frank felt an almost physical shock as the man's keen eyes swept over him. He judged the cowman to be about forty, and his mind was still dazed by Reece's glance as he realized that someone was talking to him.

"Harris!" Fowler was saying. "Mr. Reece needs a pen!"

But Reece had already reached across the desk and taken the pen from its holder. He began signing the register with a bold signature.

Fowler pushed himself forward in the crowd and said, "I can't begin to tell you how delighted we are to have you with us again, Mr. Reece."

Reece nodded as he laid the pen down on the book. He had started to turn when Harris, his throat dry, said, "Your rooms are not quite ready."

14

Those quick, keen eyes swung back to the younger man. "Why not?"

"They should be ready, Harris!" Fowler snapped.

Fearing he would lose his voice, Frank held his ground. "There is a young lady vacating the rooms. A young lady is not to be hurried." He added, "Not even for Mr. Reece." Suddenly Frank became acutely aware of the fact that Reece and every cowboy in his retinue had a large, deadly-looking revolver strapped to his waist. He remembered the shots and wild yells that had come from the street. He remembered his own statement that Reece could probably kill a man and get away with it.

"Harris!" Fowler sputtered.

Reece's expression did not change. He turned slowly toward Frank, and Harris felt his knees shake involuntarily.

Reece said, "The boy is quite right."

"It will only be a moment, I assure you," Fowler insisted. "I'll run up and see about it myself."

As Fowler hurried away, one of the cattle buyers offered Reece a cigar, and three others raced for the honor of lighting it for him. Inhaling deeply, Reece glanced from one to the other of the well-dressed buyers. "How's the beef market this season?"

"Running two and three-quarter cents," one of the buyers shrugged. "Not too good."

Harris thought he noticed the faintest trace of humor in Reece's voice as the cowman said, "Sure appreciate all your friendliness, what with the market being bad."

The strong, tough-looking Spaniard, Mendoza, said, "Maybe we ought to take the cows on to New York, boss."

The cowboys grouped around the desk laughed at Mendoza's suggestion, and then Harris noticed Fowler coming downstairs with Señor Vidal and Maria behind him.

"Your rooms will be ready in a few moments now, sir," Harris said.

At the head of a squad of bellboys, the bell captain

approached and took the bedroll that Reece had leaned, end down, on the floor. Hurrying across the lobby, Fowler said, "I'm sure you'll find everything satisfactory now, Mr. Reece."

Señor Vidal and Maria were at a level with the desk as Reece turned toward Fowler. Vidal saw Reece, and leaving Maria for a moment, walked over to the cowman. "Señor Reece," the Spaniard said, putting out his hand. "You are in Chicago with a herd?"

"That's right." Reece shook the other man's hand once and dropped it. "And you?"

"Just a visit. I'm on my way back to Chihuahua now."

"Got enough cattle down there to make it worth my time to go down?"

"Yes. Both quantity and quality."

"Then you may be seeing me soon."

Vidal moved away. "*Hasta la vista*, Señor Reece."

Harris stared over the crowd at Maria. She smiled timidly at him, and then her father was at her side and they went on toward the door.

"Just to start things off, Fowler," Reece said, "send up twenty or thirty chickens. We've been eating beef so long that Red here has started mooing and pawing the ground like a steer. Send up a couple cases of whisky. My party will start around ten-thirty. The ballroom ready?"

"Yes sir. Yes sir."

Reece frowned suddenly. "Where's Haley? I want someone around who can get things done for me."

Fowler turned his hands up in mild exasperation. "He left us two months ago. Young Harris took his place. But I thought I would go along with you, since—"

"No." Reece shook his head. "You're too close to the hotel owners, Fowler. Even when you know it'll be paid for, you wince every time a chair gets broken or a light gets shot out. I'll take the kid behind the desk."

Fowler shrugged in defeat. "As you wish, Mr. Reece. Harris, you will be personally responsible to Mr. Reece during his stay at the Royal."

Reece strode away with the others hurrying to keep

ıp with him, and Frank turned the register. It was signed,
"Tom Reece and Party."

"Well, hop to it, Harris!" Fowler ordered. "You stay
vith him. And make certain his stay is a pleasant one,
ou understand?"

"Yes, Mr. Fowler." Frank rushed toward the group
lisappearing up the stairs and fell in alongside a grizzled,
edheaded cowboy who looked at the boy's neatly tied
cravat with unconcealed contempt. From up above, as
he group poured out onto the second floor, scattered
entences and laughter drifted behind them.

"Every Indian between here and Dallas is feeding on
Flying R beef!"

"Worst trailin' ever I seen! Drought, blizzard an' stompede all the God-damned way!"

"There's just one thing keeps me from wantin' to
spend the whole night in a good, hot bath."

"Hell, Charley," someone chuckled. "Maybe we kin
get some girls to join you in the bath; then you won't
have t' leave it!"

Throughout the south wing, the cowhands scattered
into the rooms—first come, first served—and by the time
Reece stepped into his suite, only the cattle buyers, the
bell captain and Frank were with him.

"Just throw it on the chair, son," Reece told the bell
captain, and Frank was surprised to see that the captain did not hesitate, waiting for a tip. He tossed the
bedroll down and smiled. "Good to have you with us,
sir." Then he ducked out the door, shutting it behind
him.

The half-dozen buyers settled themselves about the
large room and Reece sat down to take off his boots.
"You," he called. "Your name's Harris?"

"Yes sir."

"I'd appreciate a hand with these boots. Feels like
they've become permanently attached to my legs."

Frank was sweating and puffing before the first tight
leather boot came off in his hands. Before the second
came off, the first case of whisky had been delivered,
and three bellhops had delivered several armfuls of ele-

gant clothes that Reece directed them to hang in the closets.

"Exactly how many cows do you have?" one of the buyers asked as the second boot came suddenly away, almost throwing Frank to the floor.

Reece rubbed his foot tenderly. "Sometimes I think Comanche moccasins are the most civilized footwear on the face of the earth."

Other bellhops arrived with large silver trays of chicken arranged in buffet style, and Reece waved them toward a long credenza at one wall. "Put it there." He stood up and started unbuttoning his shirt. "I've got twenty-four hundred and seventy-six head."

"Big herd," a tall, slender buyer commented.

His shirt unbuttoned, Reece went to the buffet and picked up a drumstick. "I don't have to tell you boys to help yourselves." He pulled the cork from a whisky bottle and poured a teacup full of the liquid. Taking a long drink, he said, "I figure my herd about eighty per cent grassers, ten per cent half-fats and ten per cent canners."

"Sounds like a low estimate on canners," a buyer muttered. "Usually higher."

"Probably even lower," Reece said flatly. "I'm giving you the best of it. I'll take three cents for the lot."

Harris, standing awkwardly a few feet from Reece, was completely lost in the conversation. It was meaningless to him, but he had the impression that Reece was playing a game that the cowman found mildly amusing yet intended nevertheless to win.

"We figured more like, say, two and a half cents, Tom," another buyer countered.

"Even that's a risk. Prices might drop overnight," a third said.

"Or go up." Reece emptied the teacup and put it down on the credenza. "Harris. Turn the hot water on and get me a bath ready that's nine-tenths steam. And keep my cup filled. As for the rest of you fellows, my final price is two and three-quarters. Take it or leave it."

"Maybe it'd be safer to put it off till tomorrow, when

the New York market is open," one of them said hesitantly.

"Joe's right," another agreed. "We better think it over. Look before we leap."

"You do that." Reece grinned.

Harris was coming out of the bathroom, leaving the hot water filling the tub, when the cattle buyers finished their drinks and headed for the door.

As the door closed behind them, a voice came from a darkened corner of the room, and Harris realized one of the buyers had not left. "Guess we can talk business now, Tom."

Reece stripped off his shirt and pants and headed for the bath with a bottle in one hand and the teacup in the other. "That's right, Mike. What a bunch of weak-kneed bastards!"

"I'll give you sixty-five thousand dollars for the lot. You can't afford to sit around Chicago waiting for the herd to fatten or the price to go up."

"Yeah?" Reece pulled off his underwear and stepped into the tub. "Wahoo! That'll scald the dirt right off my aching hide!"

Harris noticed several wicked scars on the cowman's leather-tough body as Reece lowered himself into the steaming water.

"What's playing at the opera, son?"

Harris said, "I—I don't know."

"Oh, my God," Reece groaned. "I picked a beaut." His eyes went over Frank again and he shook his head. "You're as skinny as a rail. Your skin is pale and your hands are soft. Most of the women out where I come from could pin you two times out of three. And on top of all that you don't even know which the hell opera's playing!"

"I'll find out, sir." Frank almost spit the final word. He stalked out of the room toward the lobby. He passed several cowboys in one stage or another of undress, and wild hoots and yells came from their rooms.

When he explained his problem to Fowler, the manager said, "Don't make the mistake of simply finding out which opera it is. Buy Mr. Reece a row of seats."

"You can't just buy a row of seats at the last minute!"

"Tell Mr. Fredericks at the ticket office who they're for. You'll get them. Have them charged to the hotel."

Half an hour later, short of breath from hurrying, Frank entered Reece's suite once more. The cowman was handsomely dressed in a splendid suit of evening clothes now, and the room was rapidly filling with a strangely mixed assortment of beautiful, worldly-looking women, cowboys, men down on their luck and wealthy businessmen.

Crossing to where Reece was standing with two lovely blondes and the cattle buyer named Mike, Frank said, "It's *La Traviata*."

Reece lifted the teacup to his lips and downed about half the whisky in it. "You get me some seats, or will I have to take care of that myself?"

"You've got the fourth row center."

"You're improving. Though I prefer the third row, son." Reece glanced through the partially open door of the bathroom and added softly, "Hand me my gun, boy. It's on the table over there."

Curious and faintly alarmed, Frank went to the table and picked up the gun. He almost dropped it. Its weight was twice what he'd expected, and the barrel looked big enough to crawl through. When he handed the revolver to Reece, the cowman stepped into the doorway to the bath and aimed quickly at the wall. A thunderous explosion blasted through the laughter and talk of the party.

"It's okay, girlie," the redheaded cowboy laughed, as a brunette near him screamed. "Reece just shot a bug of some sort. When he's livin' fancy, he hates bugs around."

Reece and the buyer named Mike were together at the door now, and as the cowman blew smoke from the gunbarrel, Mike said, "Look. I'll go up to sixty-nine thousand."

"You're ready to go seventy-three thousand, Mike. But I'm not going to waste a whole evening arguing over a few thousand. I'll let you have the whole herd for an even seventy."

"Done." The buyer took out a large wad of thousand-dollar bills and began to count.

Harris, who had never seen a bill larger than a fifty, stared with fascination. Reece did not recount. He took the thick mass of bills and jammed them into a pocket, and the two blondes stepped toward him, smiling.

"Business all done, honey?" one of them asked.

Reece nodded. "All right!" he said so that the whole room could hear him. "Who's for the opera? Let's have a little beauty and refinement before that stampede of a party starts in the ballroom!"

CHAPTER THREE

F<small>RANK</small> relieved Naylor, the night clerk at the desk, while Reece was at the opera. When Naylor came back from supper, he said, "You going to work all night, Frank?"

"Looks that way. Fowler told me to stick close to Reece while he was in the hotel. From the sound of those cowboys in the ballroom, it's going to be a long night."

"I guess Reece is one of the best cattlemen on the trail these days. Maybe the best. And rich," Naylor sighed. "He was here for a week last year. Haley was given the job you got. And before he left, Reece gave Haley a hundred dollars. More than two months' wages, just like that! You're lucky."

There was the sound of a loud, strong voice singing out on the street, and a moment later Reece and the men and women who had gone with him to the opera came into the lobby. Reece broke off in the middle of his song as he approached the desk. "Tell me," he said, "have you ever heard anything so beautiful?"

"As your voice, or the music?" Harris asked, realizing that Reece was beginning to feel the huge quantity of whisky he'd been drinking.

"Both, boy! Both!"

"The music's fine. But I'd say you make a better cowman than opera singer."

Reece grinned. "That's not a bad answer. Come on up to my suite, kid. There's something I want you to do." He put an arm around the blonde nearest him. "Go on to the ballroom. I'll join you there in a minute."

In his large room on the second floor, that had emptied as everyone drifted to the ballroom, Reece said to Frank, "I want you to set up a good-sized table in the middle of the room, here, for a poker game. Get plenty

of chips and some comfortable chairs. It will likely go
on for quite a while."

"Yes sir." Reece was heading for the door when Frank
said, "Sir?"

"Yeah?" The cowman turned, and turning noticed the
credenza. "Pour me a teacup of that elixir, son."

Handing him a fresh cup, Frank said, "I came to Chicago to get in the cattle business. I know you don't think
I'm much, but I'm stronger than I look. I was raised on
a farm, and I know animals pretty well. I can ride a
horse." He hesitated.

Reece held out the teacup for a refill. "What are you
trying to say, son?" He drank again as Harris continued.

"I want a job. I'd like to go to work for you." Once
he had said this, Frank plunged on. "I heard you gave
the last fellow who helped you out here at the hotel a
really big tip. I don't care about a tip. Matter of fact, I
hate the idea of even being offered one. If you want to
do me a favor, hire me. I can ride all day and all night!"

"For how many nights running, boy?" Reece asked
quietly. "I'm going to say this to you, and after it's
said, I don't want to hear any more about this. Agreed?"

"Yes sir."

"I take it you love the idea of outdoor life. Good,
clean, sometimes hard work with a bunch of men who
are good friends. Probably like horses, and like the idea
of a gay, carefree time when the crew hits town."

"That's right."

"Well, kid, you are a God-damned idiot." Reece spoke
flatly, but without malice. "I run into fools like you
everywhere I go. Even tried a couple of them out, back
in my more youthful days. They folded up within a
week." Warming to the subject, Reece waved the cup
at Frank. "You see us having a great time in town. We've
got more life and fun and general joy for living than any
ten city men. There's a reason for that. Any one of us
can be dead before the moon changes. This last drive
wasn't too bad, but the way we came is marked with
three graves. One Indian arrow, one stampede, and one
crazy maverick.

"As far as good fellowship, about half the boys I've got with me this trip are renegades and drifters, men who'd cut your throat for five dollars if they thought they could get away with it.

"You love horses? Well on a cattle drive a horse is a way to get someplace, that's all. Trail horses are mean and lazy, and one of their favorite occupations is kicking a man's head off so they can go on eating grass uninterrupted.

"The great, peaceful outdoors? Christ! You never knew what cold is till you get winter wind sweeping across a hundred miles of snow-covered plains just to blow icicles through your hide. You don't know what heat is, or what real dust can do to a man's eyes and nose and throat. Did you know dust can kill?"

He waited for an answer and Harris finally said, "Well, I never really thought about it."

Reece shrugged. "Well, I could go on all night, but what's the use. The answer is no. Try some other outfit."

"I've tried a couple. They turned me down."

"Don't blame them. A beginner's too much responsibility."

"I'd want it understood that I wasn't your responsibility!"

"When I'm trailing a herd, everything is my responsibility. Forget it. Fix up that poker table." Reece stared thoughtfully at the younger man. "You look like you just got hit in the back of the head with an ax."

"I—I'm sorry. I'm disappointed."

"No hard feelings, son. But my answer to you has got to be no. Some day you'll thank me." The cowman went to the door, then turned around. "After you set up the poker table, you can turn in."

"Yes sir."

Frank's eyes became bitter after he was alone in the room. He started out to find a table for the poker game. He knew by the sudden increase in noise and hilarity that came from the ballroom that Tom Reece had arrived there.

At eight in the morning, Frank left his boarding house three blocks from the Royal Hotel, and ten minutes later he approached the desk to relieve Naylor.

The other clerk looked haggard and slightly drunk. "What a night!" he moaned. "Every cowboy who came through the lobby either wanted to drink with me or fight with me."

"You better get some sleep."

"I can use it. You know, that Reece is really something." Naylor leaned forward confidentially. "He almost kicked the floor through with his dancing, and drank enough whisky to float a gunboat. But more interesting, his boys say he polished it off by making love to five women. Had them yelling uncle!"

"Oh?" Frank nodded without enthusiasm.

"And for the last five or six hours he's been in a poker game upstairs. They've bet as much as a thousand dollars on the turn of a card!"

"You look tired, Naylor. Go on home and rest."

About nine o'clock, Reece came down the stairs alone and strode across the lobby to the desk. He still looked strong and vital, but Frank noticed that his boots seemed to pound unusually hard as he walked, as though not certain how far down the floor was. He said, "Morning."

"Good morning, Mr. Reece. What can I do for you?"

Fowler came out of the office at that moment. "Ahh, Mr. Reece. Your party sounded—uh—successful."

"It was." The cowman handed Fowler a wad of bills. "I'm leaving sooner than expected. This will take care of everything. What's left over, divide up among the help. I want Harris, here, to have a hundred."

"I don't want it," Frank said flatly.

"Suit yourself." Reece turned and went back up the stairs, with Fowler following and saying how much he hated to see the cowman go.

A bellhop came over to the desk. "I just heard what happened," he told Frank in a low voice. "Reece lost his shirt in that poker game. Went through about sixty thousand dollars!"

"What?"

"Yeah. The others are still playing, but he's broke."

"Keep an eye on the desk." Frank hurried upstair and went into Reece's suite, where the cowman was idl smoking a cigar, watching five other men who were sti. in the poker game.

"Mr. Reece, can I talk to you for a minute in private?

Reece looked blank for a moment, then said, "Oh Harris. The answer's still no."

"This is different."

Reece flicked his ashes toward a saucer at his sid and missed. "All right, but make it quick."

When the two of them were in the hall, Frank spok swiftly. "Understand you're broke. Want some money?

His cigar jutting out above his square jaw, Reece folde his arms, leaned back against the door and eyed Fran suspiciously. "I'm never broke. But I am out of money.

"I've got thirty-eight hundred dollars you can have."

Reece's eyebrows twisted in cautious interest. "Where?

"In the hotel safe. I got it from the sale of our farn when my dad died."

"Well for God's sake get it out, son! It's not doin, anybody any good in a safe!"

His voice tight with eagerness, Frank said, "One mor thing. This makes us partners!"

"Partners?" Reece's lips curled back in a strong smil that tilted the cigar up. "I've never been partners witl anybody in my life."

"Those are my terms. Okay?"

"Stop jawing business and get the damn fool money!

A few minutes later, Frank shoved the money into Reece's hand. "That'll help put your outfit back on th trail. Partner."

"Don't use that word!" Reece said. "Makes me fee silly." He frowned and put out his hand. "Call m Tom."

"Yes, sir, Tom!" Frank pumped the cowman's hanc energetically.

"See you later." Reece went back into the room behind him, shutting the door.

Frank wet his lips, standing there uncertainly, and then went back to the desk. Half an hour later Fowler, who had been calming the nerves of other guests in the hotel, joined him there. "Stopped by Mr. Reece's suite," he said. "He's back in that poker game."

"He is?"

"What are you looking so horrified about?"

"Nothing, sir."

"Actually, it's been rather peaceful this time. Last year we'd had three injured men and a fire in the lobby by now."

"How is Mr. Reece doing in the poker game, sir?"

"Winning like crazy. His luck's changed." Fowler nodded affably to an elderly couple passing the desk. "But he's not changed his mind about leaving today. He and his crew will be leaving on the three o'clock train for Kansas."

Frank's throat was uncommonly tight, for he knew that the next two words he spoke were, for better or for worse, going to change his life completely. And once spoken, there would be no turning back. "Mr. Fowler," he said, "I'm quitting."

CHAPTER FOUR

At two o'clock, Frank Harris stood in front of th[e] Royal. He was hatless, and his one good suit was care[-] fully rolled into the bedroll he had slung over one shou[l-] der. He glanced at it out of the corner of his eye, the[n] glanced with quick embarrassment back toward the hote[l] door. That bedroll looked worse every time he looked a[t] it. None of Reece's men had a checkered blanket formin[g] the outside of his bedroll. But it was the only blanke[t] Frank had. Also, the roll was not trim, but lumpy an[d] out of balance. The cord that bound it looked fragil[e] and insufficient, as though it would break at the firs[t] rough handling and scatter Frank's few possessions al[l] over the street.

Harris was dressed in bib overalls that, though properl[y] beaten and old, did not have the lean, tough, romanti[c] flavor that the cowboys' working clothes had. In place o[f] boots, he was wearing the nearest thing he had, a scuffe[d] old pair of farmer brogans.

The Spaniard, Mendoza, came out of the hotel an[d] shot a hasty second look at Frank as he started by o[n] the sidewalk.

"Mr. Mendoza!" Frank called, his voice coming out more sharply than he'd intended.

Mendoza turned and gave him a long, searching look. "Oh, thought I'd seen you someplace before. What'[s] that you got over your shoulder?"

"A bedroll."

"Oh."

"Can I walk along with you?"

Mendoza's eyes swept the street swiftly, as though h[e]

vere both looking for an avenue of escape and making
ure none of his friends saw him with this strange crea-
ure. "Well, I guess so. Why?"

"I'm part of the outfit now." Frank grinned.

"You are?" There was a note of quiet desperation in
Mendoza's voice. "Since when?"

"Made a deal with Mr. Reece. Tom, that is."

The Spaniard pulled thoughtfully at his ear. "You sure
of that?"

"Yes sir!" Frank nodded.

"Well, okay. I'm goin' down to where our gear is
waiting." Mendoza moved on along the street, and Frank
fell in beside him, hurrying to keep up.

They came wordlessly to the stockyards after a few
blocks, and Mendoza wound his way through large stacks
of baled hay, corrals and pens, until at last they came to
a warehouse near the train tracks. The warehouse watch-
man nodded at Mendoza and the two men went into a
huge, earth-floored room. In one corner there was a mass
of saddles, saddle-blankets, ropes, bridles and general trail
gear. Mendoza kicked one of the saddles into a position
that was to his liking, then stretched out on the ground
with his head cushioned in the sloping seat. "Might as
well try to catch a few winks before the others get
down here."

Frank put his bedroll down gently, considered sitting
on it and decided it was too much of a risk. He was
seated on the ground near it when there was the sound
of a wagon pulling up outside, and the cumbersome
vehicle swung into sight through the wide, warehouse
doors. Reece was driving, and he pulled the stolid, two-
horse team to a halt. His crew, in various states of hang-
over, dejection and pure unconsciousness, was piled in
the back. The cowman went to the rear of the wagon,
dropped the tailgate and yelled, "Stompede! Everybody
out! Gather your gear! Train west pulls out in ten minutes!"

With his men staggering behind him, Reece entered

the warehouse and saw Frank. "What in hell you doing
here? I looked all over that hotel for you!"

Mendoza watched with sleepy interest, ignoring the
grumbling, cursing cowboys hefting saddles to shoulder
and heading for the train.

Frank forced himself to look Reece straight in the eye.
"I'm going with you."

"I told you I wasn't hiring you!"

"I'm not an employee. I'm a partner."

"Oh, my God!" Reece rubbed a hand over his face.
"Look, kid, you helped me out in a poker game when
I'd had too much to drink to know black from white.
I got five thousand here that pays you back with damned
good interest." He took the money from his pocket. "Now
beat it. Go back to the hotel."

"I quit my job there," Frank said firmly. "You knew
very well that I was buying into your outfit when I gave
you that money."

"Oh, Christ!" Reece muttered. "Spare me moments
like this! You're making a twelve-hundred-dollar profit.
What more do you want?"

"I'm going with you."

Mendoza stood up and shouldered his saddle. "The
kid's right, boss."

"Who asked you?" Reece roared.

"Nobody." Mendoza shrugged. "But if he wasn't right,
you'd have killed him by now." He started hiking toward
the train.

At that instant the train whistle screamed a warning
note and people began hurrying to get aboard.

"We better get going, don't you think?" Frank said.

Reece glowered at him. "All right! But you won't last
a week!" He jammed the money into his pocket. "That
five thousand is yours! You can collect it and pull out
any time!"

Frank smiled happily. "Okay, Tom!"

"And don't call me Tom! My name is Reece!" The
cowman threw his own saddle to his shoulder and noticed

 one lying in the shadowy corner. "That God-damned Red forgot his leather! Bring it!" He picked the saddle up with his free hand and tossed it to Frank. The weight of the thing almost knocked Frank down, but he hoisted it up, imitating Reece. His checkered bedroll clutched under his other arm, he followed the swiftly striding cowman toward the train that now had its steam up. After ten steps a leather ridge on the saddle began to bite savagely into Frank's shoulder each time he came down on his right foot.

Beyond the warehouse, Reece whirled and called back angrily over the few feet that separated them, "Just how big a chunk of me do you figure you bought?"

"I'll trust you to figure that. Thirty-eight hundred ought to go quite a way."

"The hell it ought! Thirty-eight hundred wouldn't keep me in cigars for a year!"

"Whatever you say, Reece."

Raging half to himself, Reece snorted as he continued toward the train. "Christ! I've ridden this country for nearly twenty-five years. Sweated and worked over every track and trail and gopher hole from here to the Rio Grande! You figure you bought a share in that?"

"I only bought what it seemed you were willing to sell."

"Yeah? And I've got four arrow holes in various places in my hide, and I'm carrying two lead slugs inside me right now! How much percentage do you get of that?"

"You can figure it however suits you," Frank panted, struggling to keep up. "Seems to me partners ought to trust each other, don't you think?"

"Partners?" Reece bellowed. "Don't ever call me that again, you God-damned—" Several words were cut out as the train whistle screamed again. "You are, in short, the juniorest God-damned partner I ever hope to see! I give you a week to be crying for your money and a ticket back to Chicago!" He reached the train and sprang up onto the platform.

Frank threw the saddle and bedroll onto the platform
and clambered up as the train began to chug out of the
station. His right shoulder was raw where the saddle had
bitten into it during the long, fast walk.

But the smile on his face was broad.

CHAPTER FIVE

IT WAS a two-day ride to the tiny junction of Frazier, Kansas, where the crew was to pick up horses for the ride back down to Texas. During this time, Frank got to know a few of the men he was now working with.

Reece, of course, was a law unto himself. He won at poker, made the best jokes, and observed more than any other man. Yet even in his best moods, he was never really one of the boys. Even while laughing with them, there was a quality and a strength to him that made him, without trying to be, more than they were. He ignored Frank.

Mendoza was Frank's favorite among the cowhands. Under his leathery, tough exterior there was a soft, fatherly man, and in his own rough way he tried to be kind to Harris, to teach him and help him.

Peggy, the only man in the lot who had a ring of fat around his middle, was pleasant and not very bright. But Frank gathered that Peg was one of the best camp cooks in the Southwest.

Slim, Charley and Joe Capper were men who would always be cowboys. They loved the work—proved by the great detail and time they spent in complaining about it—and didn't have the ambition or drive necessary to strike out on their own in any direction. Frank liked them, and they accepted him with easy indifference.

Of the others, Red was the only one who made a lasting impression on Frank. It was negative. The first night out of Chicago, Red leaned back in his seat and stared across the aisle at Frank. "Hey, kid," he called in a high, nasal voice. "How come you're with us? Somebody lose at cards and collect you as booby prize?"

Frank grinned self-consciously, wanting to take the hazing like a good sport. "No, I'm just a down-payment on a booby prize."

Red measured the others' laughter and guessed the comeback was better than his joke. This irritated him. Leaning forward he said, "Now, kid. You don't plan to be no cowpoke? You're so skinny some mare might take you for a horsefly and kill you with a flick of her tail." He added solemnly, "Matter of fact, a fair-sized Texas horsefly might fly off with you in the first place."

Frank grinned again, but this time it was forced. "I'll watch out for the horseflies, Red." He turned away and hoped that the other man would let it go at that.

"As I see it, ain't nothin' funnier-lookin' than you ever headed for Kansas, except maybe that bundle you got stowed up on the baggage shelf. What'd you wrap it in? A wet checkerboard?"

Not answering this time, Frank smiled sheepishly and turned away once more.

"Let's open 'er up and see what's inside." Red stood and started for Frank's bedroll.

"I wish you'd leave it alone," Frank said.

"Why, baby boy? You got a tintype of your ma in it?"

"Among other things, yes."

"From the funny shape to it," somebody called to Red, "it looks like he's got his ma inside it!"

"My God, you just might be right!" Red stretched his hands up to grab the checkered bedroll, and Frank stood up to stop him, almost losing his balance between his nervousness and the sway of the train.

Red shoved him back down into the seat with a sudden push of his hand, and before Frank could get up, Mendoza was facing Red.

"Leave the boy's gear alone," he said quietly.

"This your business?"

"Looks that way."

"You're bitin' off more'n you can chew."

"Maybe."

Reece chose that moment to come back into the car from the rear platform, where he'd been smoking a cigar by himself. He glanced at the two men and said, "What's the problem?"

Red glared at Mendoza briefly, then turned to Reece. "Nothin'." He walked back to his seat and sat down.

"Good." Reece grabbed a strap and stood in the swaying car as it jolted along through the night. "This damn train is problem enough. Gaps between rail-ends as much as five inches wide."

"What was the final count on cows that got knocked flat and trampled to death in the cattle cars, when we was goin' up to Chicago from Frazier Junction?" one of the crew asked.

"Eighty-seven," Reece grumbled.

"Look out!" someone yelped in angry panic.

"Oh hell!" Charley broke into muffled laughter. "I'm sorry, Singer. Didn't mean to spit tobacco on your new boots." He hoisted one of Singer's legs up onto the back of the seat before them. "Did everybody get a chance to see Singer's purty new boots?"

"You buy 'em yourself?" Slim demanded, "or did that redhead in Chicago give 'em to you as a hint to keep movin'?"

The joking turned toward Singer and his new boots, now, and Frank looked up at Mendoza. "Thanks," he said.

The Spaniard shrugged. "Look out for Red. He's a mean one."

Frazier Junction was a few small buildings in the middle of an immense prairie that was divided down the center by the railroad tracks. The Flying R men clambered off the train and it chugged on its way, slowly gaining speed.

Frank noticed that two large open wagons were drawn up by the station platform. Mendoza told him, "Those will take us out to where the horses and chuckwagon are waiting. Throw your stuff in one of them."

As Frank put his bedroll in a wagon, two men came from across the street to meet Reece. One of them shook hands and said, "Hi, boss. This here's the new hand I hired. Name of Doc Bender."

"You got my wire all right then?"

"Yeah."

Reece studied the other man, and Frank stared at him with fascination. Bender was about Reece's age, quiet and self-contained. But more than that, and the thing that fascinated Frank, was the unexplainable aura of calm deadliness about him.

"You got quite a reputation, Bender," Reece said. "I was looking to hire a good cowhand, not a gunman."

Bender nodded with quiet understanding. "I can see how you'd feel about that, Reece. Truth is, I'm a fair hand working cattle. You're not hiring my gun, and I'm not intending to use it."

"Last I heard of you, you were marshal over at Wichita. What happened to that job?"

"I quit."

Reece nodded briefly. "All right." Turning to the other man he said, "Everything ready out at the corral, Curtis?"

"Yeah."

"Good. We're going to try for another drive before winter hits. There's stuff to be picked up in Mexico."

"Shall we roll?"

"Soon's I get off a couple wires." Reece headed up the platform toward the stationmaster's office.

"Say, kid." Red's voice came from behind Frank in little more than a whisper.

Turning, Frank saw the redhaired man standing only a step away. There was a gun in his hand, and it was pointed straight down, held easily in the man's big hand. "What, Red?"

"Well, I gave you some trouble on the train." Red's eyes dropped as though he were embarrassed.

"That's okay. Forget it."

"No, I don't wanna forget it. I feel bad about it. An' I thought maybe I could do somethin' to kinda make things up."

"No need for that."

"I'll bet you ain't got no gun."

"No. I haven't."

"Well," Red said, his face wrinkling in a grin. "Then maybe I can help you like I hoped. The thing is, I got me a good gun, an' I got this here old Moore six-shooter,

for a spare. It's a damn fine gun, worth thirty dollars if
it's worth a dime. But I'd be glad to leave you have it for,
say five dollars. You got to have a gun, what with mountain lions and snakes and Indians. Hell, the only reason
I'm practically givin' it to you is that I feel kinda bad
about the way I talked to you."

The thought of owning a gun appealed to Frank. Red
saw this and handed the gun to him.

"She shoots like a dream."

The gun looked a little odd to Frank, different from the
few he'd seen, and it was definitely old. But the feel of it
in his hand was irresistible. "All right, I'll take it. And
thanks, Red." He fumbled in his pocket for the money
and handed it to the other man.

"Why don't you shoot it right now? See how she
works?"

"Right here?"

"Well, no." Red hesitated. "I guess you're right. Be a
good idea to take it down the track a ways. Just pull back
the hammer to cock her, and pull the trigger. She's all
loaded."

Red walked with him to the end of the platform, where
the planking angled down to the ground. "I'll stay here
and watch. You just go ahead. Pick out your target and
blast away."

Frank walked another twenty feet from the end of the
platform. He pulled back the hammer, and the cylinder
rotated with a businesslike click into position. Holding
the revolver carefully, he stretched out his arm and aimed
at a small rock a few yards away. When he judged he'd
hit pretty close, he gently pulled the trigger.

And the whole world exploded.

There was a giant, blinding flash, and for a terrifying,
roaring instant, he saw red and white stars racing wildly
before his eyes. When the stars faded out, he couldn't see
anything. By blinking, he got a few glimpses of light, and
he reached his free hand up to wipe his eyes. The hand
touched warm blood, but it cleared his vision a little. The
right eye could see only blurred, dim patterns, but his
left eye now was clear. Vaguely he was now becoming

aware that his right arm was stiff and sore and burned, and that the pain increased along the arm to the hand, which was numb with agony. As the shock ebbed away, he realized that the gun had exploded in his hand. He didn't even dare look at the hand for fear it was mutilated —or blown off.

He turned back toward the platform and saw Red doubled over with laughter. Red made two serious mistakes: he underestimated Frank's rage, and he underestimated the strength that rage gave him.

As Frank walked quickly toward him, he managed to stifle his laughter somewhat and prepare for some small trouble.

The trouble came in the form of a clenched left fist that rushed out with tremendous speed and caught him in the middle of his face. Red was staggered back by the unexpected force of the blow. His left leg went back for support and came down beyond where the platform ended. Red dropped out of sight and landed with a heavy thud on the tracks five feet below.

Frank was just getting started. His right eye was clear enough now to give him better perspective, and he wiped blood away from his forehead as he jumped to the tracks beside Red. When Red started to get up, Frank hit him again with his left, then swung savagely with his right. The right landed solidly on the side of the other man's head, and pain shot up Frank's arm to the elbow. But it was worth it to see Red flop back onto the ties between the tracks, his face starting to bleed.

Red tried to get up three times to rush Frank, but each time Harris caught him with a left and then that formidable right that sent him flying back. And then someone was between them, forcing Frank back and away. He recognized Reece's voice shouting, "Stop it before you kill the bastard!"

Blood covered Frank's eyes again now, and someone helped him sit down on a steel rail. He heard Mendoza's voice saying, "You'll be all right, kid. You're better off than the other one."

The Spaniard rubbed a cloth over Frank's eyes, clearing

them again. Frank looked down at his throbbing right
hand. It looked different. As his senses cleared, he realized
he was holding what was left of the six-shooter in his
hand.

Mendoza started to ease the broken gun out of Frank's
hand. "That cylinder and stub of a gunbarrel makes the
meanest pair of brass knuckles I ever saw," the Spaniard
muttered. "You like to killed that poor son of a bitch."
Examining the gun, he called over his shoulder, "There
was a plug in the barrel, Reece. Had to be to break it off
like this."

Frank was aware that Red was on his feet, leaning back
against the platform for support, and Reece was counting
out some money. "You're fired. I can't stand a man with
a sense of humor different from mine."

Red staggered away toward the buildings of the town,
and Reece came to stand in front of Frank. "You'd be
fired, too, if I had any brains! You'd be fired on the
grounds of being so God-damned stupid!"

"I'm sorry," Frank mumbled. "That's the first fight I
was ever in. I didn't know I was hitting him with the
gun. Didn't mean to."

"It's a good thing you did, or he'd have busted you
in two," Reece said angrily. He turned toward the men
lining the platform. "Let's get in those wagons! We got
work to do!"

CHAPTER SIX

Mendoza took a small, metal flask of whisky from one of his saddlebags as the wagon rumbled slowly over the rutted trail leading to the flatlands out of town. He stepped over the men sitting in the back of the wagon and knelt down beside Frank. Pouring a few drops of the liquid into his hand, he rubbed the burning stuff over the cut in Frank's forehead. "Not deep. Bleeding stopped already, just about. How's the hand?"

"I can move it now. Nothing's broken."

"You sure whipped the ass off old Red," Charley said. "Served him right."

"Well, give a listen to preacher Charley," Slim grunted. "You saw him spike that old blunderbuss."

"So did you."

Slim shrugged and began to roll a cigarette. Frank noticed, with a shock born of reading too much about fictitious Westerners, that Slim spilled at least as much tobacco as finally wound up in the cigarette.

About two miles out of Frazier, the wagons pulled to a stop near a large, makeshift corral in which about sixty horses were milling. A covered chuckwagon was standing in the shade of a cottonwood nearby. Two men had been lolling in the shade, and as Reece hopped down from the seat of the lead wagon, they walked over to him. The cowman exchanged a few words with them, then walked to the tree where a big, powerfully muscled black gelding was tied and waiting. He swung into the saddle and hauled the gelding around to walk it back to where the men were now pulling out of the wagons.

"Each man pick himself a string of horses," Reece said. "Peggy, whip up some beans. We'll be leaving in an hour."

Uncertain what to do, his head beginning to ache al-

ost as much as his hand, Frank wandered toward the
orral. He had never seen so much confusion, yet in a
bewildering way the chaos made sense.

Cowboys were yelling and hooting all around him as
they flicked rawhide lariats into the churning mass of
horses. Within seconds the dust was so thick that Frank
could hardly make out one rushing beast from another.
Some of the men were ducking into the corral from time
to time, which to Frank looked like plain suicide, and
others were hauling lassoed ponies out of the gate a few
feet away. For the first time, Frank felt defeated and
helpless. What could he do? Even if he could use a rope
in the second place, he didn't have one in the first place.

Slim whistled shrilly a few feet away, and the blasting
note made a nearby gray horse wheel away, tossing its
head high. In the instant its neck arched up, Slim's rope
shot out and snapped into a tight loop high on its neck,
just behind the jaw and ears. Keeping the line taut, Slim
hauled the gray slowly through the others toward the
gate. Once the animal was out, Slim led it to a ground
stake he'd sunk into the earth a few feet away and teth-
ered it near two other horses he'd already taken out. He
threw a saddle on one of them and began tightening the
cinch strap, and Frank walked over to him.

"Say Slim, can I borrow your rope?"

Slim threw a hitch into the cinch strap and glanced
up at the younger man. "What for?"

"To catch me some horses."

"Well—" Slim took the thick, wooden stirrup off the
pommel and dropped it into position. "It's agin my better judgment. But I guess so." He handed the tough
rawhide rope to Frank. "You bust it, and I'll bust your
head."

As Harris went back to the corral, he saw with amazement that only a few horses were left. Charley and Singer
each had a loop around an animal. They hauled them out
of the gate as Frank came up, and Singer slammed the
gate shut.

There were only four horses left now, and Joe Capper

hopped over the fence at the far side and threw a loop
easily over the neck of a placid paint. Now there wer
only three.

Reece rode up so close to Frank that the black's hoof
touched the wide brogans. "I see you've picked the thre
horses you want on your string," he said.

"Looks that way, doesn't it."

"Now just what the hell are you going to do with them
now that you got them?"

"Don't quite know."

Reece turned to look behind him. "Also, I'm sending
those two wagons back to Frazier. Is it part of your pla
to have your bedroll go back too?"

Glancing quickly around, Frank saw that two men were
driving the wagons away. Still sitting in the rear wagon
was his checkered bedroll. "Oh, hell!" He dropped the
rope and sprinted after his rapidly disappearing gear. Hop
ping into the moving wagon, he lifted the roll onto one
shoulder and quickly leaped back out. That was when the
thin cord broke.

The checkered blanket sagged loosely over Frank's
shoulder, as both ends popped open and scattered his
things along the dusty ground.

A dozen cowboys, most of them already mounted
gathered in a circle around him as he struggled to gather
his possessions.

"Poor fellow busted his bedroll," Capper said sadly.

Those who were laughing broke off in barely controlled
snickers as it became apparent that his misfortune was to
be considered a first-class tragedy.

"Interestin', the things a man carries," Singer said
"Young fellow had the foresight to bring along his alarm
clock, I see. No more lyin' in bed till four o'clock in the
mornin'."

"Maybe he's got it timed to go off in case of Indian
attack or stampede," another suggested. "Be mighty re-
assurin', havin' him along with us with that alarm clock."

"An' look at them there tintypes. And three readin'
books, by God!"

"He's got culture and class, I'd say."

"Maybe he can read to you, Benson, seein' you can't
d nohow."

"Neither can you, you bastard!"

"Hey!" Capper shouted as Frank gathered up his good
t and shoes. "Lookit that fancy outfit. Plumb forgot
's used to fancy livin' in Chicago. You know, boy, you
uld make more money rentin' out that suit than
wboyin'!"

Reece at last rode through the group. "What are you
ing to do, Harris? Make this whole outfit the laughing
ck of the southwest?"

Frank looked up from the dust. "No sir." He was in-
ntly sorry he'd called Reece sir, but the words were
eady out. He was beginning to hate everyone there.
urderous practical jokes. Witless teasing. No one ever
ed to simply help a newcomer. They ganged up on you
e a bunch of animals.

"Peggy!" Reece roared, and the cook came from the
uckwagon at a lope. "Someplace in that wagon, you
t an old outfit of mine. Dig up a gun and some cowboy
ls for this idiot. Saddle, lariat, bridle. And for Christ's
te get him a decent bedroll!"

"Thanks, Reece," Frank said.

"Don't thank me! Every penny'll come out of your
ges!"

"You mean I'm drawing wages? I thought we—"

"Don't say it!" Reece growled. "I mean you'll pay for
y gear I give you, one way or the other."

"That's the way I want it."

"And you better be ready to ride out of here with the
t of us. We're not waiting for anyone or anything."

Peggy found clothes, plus boots and a hat for Frank,
d while Harris was putting them on, the cook produced
saddle and some other gear. "That oughta hold you,
nny," he said. He went back to stirring a large pot of
ans.

When Frank got back to the corral, Mendoza was wait-
g for him. The Spaniard shook his head. "You couldn't

have got a worse three horses if Reece himself had pick
'em for you. The geldin's lame. One mare's unbroke, a
the other ain't seen saddle in two years."

"Which one should I start with?"

"Best try the steeldust. At least she can move, a
maybe she won't kill you."

"That's encouraging." Frank took the hemp rope
now owned from his rugged, worn saddle and entered t
corral. "Which one's the steeldust?"

"The blue roan."

"Which is the blue roan?"

Mendoza rolled his eyes skyward. "The darkest hors
And watch out for that rope! Don't twirl it with yo
fingers! Roll the loop around with your wrist!"

With the Spaniard giving advice, Frank got a li
around the mare's neck on the second try. It settled t
far down her neck and when she took off it was like tryi
to hold a locomotive. He was pulled off his feet and t
hemp hissed through his hands like an angry snake, taki
a painful amount of skin with it. Then the mare mac
the tactical mistake of turning and backing away from hi
and the rope moved up her neck. The line still in h
hands, Frank jumped back onto his feet as Mendoz
yelled, "Hold 'er tight now and reel her in a little!"

Panting from the tug-of-war, Frank at last got the ma
tied on a short line to a fencepost. He grabbed his saddl
by the horn and was about to toss it on her back whe
Mendoza stopped him. "That's no plug, kid. Show '
the saddle first, and talk to 'er. Talk nice. Even sing
little. Scratch her belly under the foreleg. She'll like tha
She can't reach it too good with her mouth, and can
get to it at all with her tail. You want to ride her, you g
to either make friends with her or knock 'er flat with
two-by-four. You can't just step up."

"Well, I'm in kind of a hurry. Looks like everybod
else is about ready to go." Frank's gaze swung around th
flats beyond the corral where some of the men were smol
ing, stretched out on the ground, or finishing their plate
of beans.

'You and me are willin' to hurry. She ain't."

A sudden thought hit Frank. "Peggy didn't give me
addle blanket!"

'That's one of Reece's old saddles. A good one, buf-
o hide with a sheepskin underlinin'. Don't need no
nket." Mendoza paused, watching as Frank gingerly
atched the mare's belly. "You ain't took a minute out
think about it an' got scared of that mare have you?"

'No." Frank showed the mare the saddle and eased
onto her back with no trouble. Cinching it tight, he
:d the bridle. She balked at the bit briefly, but he per-
•ded her to take it, and then the bridle was on.

'Well, here goes."

'No." Mendoza shook his head and spoke in a low
:ce. "Everybody's watchin' you, and expectin' you to
id up underneath. They'd murder me for tellin' you
s, but the mare's a blower. That cinch is loose. Tighten
again."

'Oh." Frank put his hand on the cinch strap and found
was no longer tight. "Thanks."

As he pulled at the leather again, Mendoza sighed.
laybe I better take the top off her for you. She's got a
an roll to her eye."

'I'll do it. I've got to." Frank swung up and shook the
ose free of her head. She wheeled and started at a dead
a for the far side of the corral.

'Grab the horn!" Mendoza yelled. "To hell with fancy
ff!"

The steeldust stopped just short of the far fence and
ink kept going. He hit the dirt and rolled into a post
l lay there blinking dirt from his eyes, trying to get
ne air back into his body. Then he realized he'd uncon-
ously held onto the reins.

'You still got 'er," Mendoza called.

'Or she's still got me," Frank muttered.

Five times in five minutes Frank was thrown to the
und, each time with more shattering force than the
t. He went over her head twice, off the side once and
:r her rump once. And the last time he couldn't quite

figure which way he'd gone, though he clearly reme
bered a hoof flashing by his face so close he'd felt t
movement of air.

A crowd had gathered to watch, and he was no long
paying attention to the hoots and yells that accompani
each spill. Now, as he struggled to his feet once mo
he saw Reece sitting his black just outside the fence.

"You trying to learn how to ride or how to fly?"

Frank didn't answer. He just spit some dirt out of h
mouth.

"You got about ten more minutes. Time for about t
more nosedives."

Frank discovered some dirt packed under his upp
lip, and he spit that out.

"You look awful. You want your money back?"

Frank picked his hat up and crushed it down on h
head. He went to the place where Mendoza had caug
and was holding the mare.

"Will you grab the horn?" the Spaniard pleaded.

"Not sportin'," Frank panted.

"This ain't a game! You'll get your head knocked o
Any smart puncher'll grab for leather if need be!"

Shaking his head stubbornly, Frank pulled himself bac
into the seat and Mendoza let go. The mare sunfishe
once and Frank crashed down at Mendoza's feet.

"Hell, boy, I lost count how many times you gor
down. You don't hold that horn pretty quick, you won
be able to climb aboard."

"Will you catch her for me?"

His screaming muscles protesting at every move, Fran
lifted his foot to the stirrup and heaved himself up. H
right hand stayed clenched with grim desperation on th
horn as the mare reared and threw herself forward wit
plunging force and kicked out wildly with her hind hoof
She whirled, sidestepped and arched into a sunfishin
dive, and still Frank was with her. She lunged into
kicking run and stopped so abruptly she almost sat dowr
Then, as though a fine idea had occurred to her, she stoo
still in deep thought, opened her mouth and reached he

ad around to take a bite out of Frank's leg. He leaned
wn and punched her in the nose as hard as he could.

Mendoza walked up beaming and said, "That's better.
think she likes you."

The Flying R crew moved out on time, hoofs rumbling
d kicking up dust, the chuckwagon rattling with a
erry lack of rhythm.

Frank somehow wound up riding far back, where the
ist was thickest. He was no longer smiling. But he was
ere.

CHAPTER SEVEN

THAT NIGHT Frank ate like a starving man, the gnawin[g] hunger within him even stronger than the pain in his leg[s] and butt, or the exhaustion that hung over him like [a] heavy, warm blanket.

He unstrapped his gun and put it over the pommel o[f] his saddle, as he noticed Doc Bender had done. The[n] he started to pull off his boots, gave up and lay back o[n] his blankets with his head cradled in the unbelievab[ly] comfortable saddle. As he drifted off into a deliciou[s] sleep, he was vaguely aware of someone standing besid[e] him, and a boot reached out and shook his shoulde[r.] "Harris."

Opening one eye, he could see by the light of th[e] campfire that Slim was standing above him. "What?"

"Thought I'd come get my lariat, if you don't mind."

A chill born of panic and disgust for himself grippe[d] Frank as he remembered borrowing the rope from Slim[.] "My God, Slim," he mumbled. "I left it behind."

"Well, there ain't no stores around here to buy a new[w] one. Guess you'll have to go back and get it."

Foreing himself to sit up, Frank said, "I'm sorry, Slim[.] I couldn't find my way there in the dark."

The standing man was silent for a long moment, and then he snorted with dry good will. "It's okay, kid. I picked it up when I saw you drop it. Just wanted to im-press on you not to leave things behind. Like I say, ain't no stores around here."

Bender, stretched out near Frank, waited until Slim had gone back to the campfire. He said, "Tough day for you?"

"Yeah."

"It'll get worse." The words were matter of fact, edged with kindness. "But then it'll get better."

"Can't get worse." Frank put his head down once more. He figured he was just starting to drift off to sleep

48

when there was a stirring and fuss throughout the camp and someone yelled, "Breakfast! Come an' get it 'fore it's gone!"

"But I just lay down!" Raising himself on his elbow, Frank could see dim light breaking in the east. "It can't be morning!"

Bender sat up and stretched. "You just had what is known as a sound night's sleep, son."

The first full day on the trail, Frank was afraid he would die. At the end of his second full day, he was afraid he wouldn't. He was settling down to sleep, too exhausted to stand in line for beef and beans, when Mendoza walked over to him with a cup of vile-smelling liquid in his hands. "This will be good for you," the Spaniard told him.

"To drink?" Frank gasped.

"No. Take off your britches and I'll rub it on. It's a mixture of salt water and whisky."

"My legs and rump are too sore to take off my pants. I can hardly move my shoulders and neck, and they're not even touching the saddle."

"Your skin's been chewed up pretty good by now. This'll burn, but it'll toughen you."

Frank took off his boots and pants. Lying face down on the blanket he said, "Whoooh!" as Mendoza applied the liquid generously.

"Burn, huh?"

"Like hot coals. I'd be screamin' if I had the strength."

"Feel better pretty quick."

"Jesus," Frank mumbled, the burning keeping him only half awake. "Doesn't Reece ever give us a rest? I've been in the saddle from before sunup to after sundown two days running."

"So've the rest of us. Including Reece."

"Maybe he's used to it. I'm not."

Slim spoke from where he was sitting not far away. "Reminds me, Harris. I was supposed to tell you your turn's come up for night ridin'."

"Huh?"

"Four hours. Eight to midnight."

Frank looked at him for a long time, half hoping he was a bad dream that would go away. "I can't do it, Slim. I can't keep my eyes open, let alone get on a horse again."

"Well," Slim ventured with mild interest, "that's okay by me. I'll ride your time for you."

"You would?" Frank's eyes drooped and his head went down onto his arms.

"For a dollar. Cash."

"You—you got a deal," Frank whispered, almost asleep as he spoke. He fumbled wearily to pull his pants up as Mendoza finished rubbing the burning solution into his hide. He handed Slim a dollar. And then he flopped over asleep. . . .

At eight o'clock someone shook his shoulder. "Wake up."

"Wha—what?" Frank mumbled groggily. He forced his eyes open and saw Reece leaning over him. "Whatsa matter?"

"Why aren't you out with the remuda?"

"Tired. Slim's ridin' for me. Made a deal with him."

"Oh?" Reece's voice tightened. "You do your own work and forget about making deals. If you can't pull your weight in this outfit, just say so and you can have your money back. Right now."

Pure anger rose up in Frank and forced the sleepiness from his eyes. "I told you I didn't want my money back."

"All right. Then get out there and go to work."

Glaring at Reece, Frank pushed himself to a sitting position. His arms aching with the strain, he pulled his boots on and stood up, weaving like a drunk man for a moment. He caught his balance and faced Reece squarely. "There's one thing you ought to know."

Reece said quietly. "I'm listening."

"You can't break me. Rate you're going, you'll maybe kill me, but you can't break me." He gritted his teeth against the effort and hoisted his saddle to his shoulder. Then he walked painfully out of the circle of firelight.

As he disappeared, Mendoza spoke in a low voice from

where he lay near Reece in the shadows. "He thinks you're trying to break him. Funny. When you're only trying to build him up."

Reece struck a match to a cigar. "Who says I'm trying to build him up?"

"I do. Anybody else made a deal like that, you wouldn't give it a second thought."

Reece waved the flame of the match out, dropped it on the ground and stepped on it. "You like him, don't you?"

"He'll do."

"Maybe so." Reece nodded. "Yes, maybe he will."

Over the next days, Frank's skin went from a state of agony to numbness, and then the numbness went away and he was all right. As they headed south they ran into two days of rain. At first Frank was beside himself with joy. The cooling drops settled the choking dust and made him feel refreshed and vibrant with new life. He sang a few notes of a song he'd heard the others singing. "*Oh, Sam Bass was born in Indiana, that was his native home. And at the age of seventeen, young Sam began to roam—*"

A filly in the remuda ahead took a notion to head east by her lonesome, and Frank clucked his mare into an easy lope, headed the filly off and drove her back into the herd. The saddle and the mare felt right under him, and the drops of rain proved there was a heaven above.

"Mendoza, this is the life!" he called to the Spaniard riding drag behind him.

Mendoza grinned, but remained quiet, a motionless, efficient hump on his horse.

Frank decided to raise his face to the worsening rain and open his mouth to taste a few drops. It was a mistake. The back of his hatbrim was tipped down by the move, and water ran from the hat down his neck. Suddenly the rain didn't feel too cool any more. It felt real cold. A stout wind now whipped across the flats, turning the raindrops into stinging pellets traveling almost level with the ground. Frank put on the waterproof leather jacket that was part of his gear, but even with that he was blue with cold inside half an hour. Then lightning and thunder came. The storm was still raging, scaring the spooky remuda into stomping, plunging, dangerous foolishness, when they made camp that night.

Chilled to the bone, Frank wondered what would be done about sleeping, since the land was an ankle-deep sea of mud. He finished his rain-soaked beans and put the tin plate back on the lowered chuckwagon gate. Drinking his steaming coffee, he saw a few of the boys get ready to turn in. They did nothing about the mud. They spread their bedrolls on the mucky ground as usual, crawled in and put their hats over their faces.

"What you thinkin', son?" Doc Bender asked him.

"Nothing much. Now I know why the outside blanket on a bedroll's made of canvas."

"Yeah. Keeps the wet out. More or less."

"Wouldn't it be better to use tents?"

"For bad weather. Little sprinkle like this isn't worth it."

There was a tremendous blast, and at the same instant a wide, flickering bolt of blue-white lightning shot between the sky and the earth a few hundred feet away.

Above the high-pitched screaming of horses in the remuda, someone bellowed, "Look out! They're headed into camp!"

Charging out of the shadows, Frank could see what looked like a solid wall of horses lunging toward him. Dropping his coffee cup, he made one headlong dive that brought him under the chuckwagon. He crouched there, hugging the earth, as the wagon trembled and shook. Horses' hoofs churned the ground close enough for him to reach out and grab them, and then it was all over. He crawled out from under the wagon and saw Reece and Doc Bender standing on the far side of it, where they had been out of the way of the stampeding animals.

"You got half the mud in the world on you," Bender grinned.

"The other half I already swallowed."

"Never flatten out that way," Reece told him. "There wasn't much to worry about with those horses. Most of them would sooner break their leg than step on you. But cattle'd just as soon run over you as flat ground. They'd have flattened the chuckwagon. Always stay in a position where you can jump someplace else." He turned to the routed camp, where men were cursing over their trampled bedrolls or wandering back toward the fire that was still burning. Peggy was muttering, "Damn, stupid, pea-brained horses," as he held up a flattened, mutilated pan.

"Round up something to ride," Reece ordered. "We'll have to track down those runaways."

"How long will it take?" Frank asked Doc Bender.

"Couple, three hours at least. Maybe all night."

Frank scratched his head, and his fingers came away covered with mud. "An' I thought rain was a nice thing. Isn't there anything on the trail that's a real blessing?"

"Yeah," Doc said. "The end of it."

CHAPTER EIGHT

THEY continued south, through the Great Plains, and one morning Slim looked at a distant, flattened mountain jutting shallowly into the sky. "Black Mesa," he told Frank. "We're in the Indian Nations."

"What's that?"

"What's that?" Slim asked in astonishment. He was chewing tobacco that morning, and he aimed a squirt at an antbed beneath his horse's hoofs. "That's where half the murderous savages in the Wild West hang out, that's what it is. Just keep a sharp eye out for some fellow with long hair, no clothes and little hatchets in their hands. That'll be Choctaws, figurin' on havin' you for breakfast."

Slim spurred ahead to keep the horse herd from fanning down a narrow draw, and Mendoza said, "Don't pay no attention to him. They're tame Indians up here in the Territory. The mean ones are farther south. Comanches."

"What are the ones up here?"

"Oh, Seminole. Not many of them. Chickasaw, Choctaw, Creek, Cherokee, mostly."

"They all sound pretty mean, just from their names."

"They was, one time. These days the weather is a bigger bother than them."

Nevertheless, Frank's heart thumped under his shirt when two days later he topped a hill before the remuda and saw a solitary teepee standing on the sloping range before him. Indians! The name repeated itself in his mind as he sat stunned, but intrigued. Indians! Indians! Good Lord above, what more could a man ask than to gaze across a grassy plain and see some real, live Indians standing by their teepee?

There were only four of them—two men, a woman and a child playing in the dirt. A swaybacked horse grazed lazily a few yards from the pointed tent, and a dog yapped incessantly to let its master know it had seen Frank.

Reece rode up alongside Frank as the two male Indians started walking toward the rise. "Chickasaw," he said. "Don't fool with 'em or they'll steal you blind."

Peggy gave the two scrawny warriors a pound of bacon and some salt, and the Flying R crew moved on. . . .

Frank couldn't see how anyone knew it when they crossed the Texas border, but cross it they did. Slim explained, "I was born and bred in Texas. And the minute you cross that line, there is a special smell to the air that only Texas has."

Capper slapped a horsefly from his gelding's neck and said, "The smell of skunk?"

"No," Slim told him. "More like fresh cow droppings." He shook his head. "I do love this here state of mine."

The Flying R ranch was in north Texas, not far from Wichita Falls. It was a twenty-two-thousand acre spread with a big, raw bunkhouse and a two-story main house backed up by two large barns and a half-acre corral. They were there only two days, long enough for Reece to take care of some ranch business, and for the cowhands to do any mending or preparing necessary for the long trip down to Chihuahua. Frank had time to sew up a tear in his left stirrup strap and finish breaking his second mare under the watchful eyes of Mendoza. Not being ridden, the lame gelding had recovered from what the Spaniard believed had been a thrown stifle, so Frank's string was in pretty fair shape.

By the time they'd traveled two-thirds of the way through the immense, sprawling prairies that were Texas, Frank had filled out until he found that Reece's old clothes almost fit him. The shirt was a little wide through the shoulders, he decided one morning after washing himself in a creek, but not much.

Reading his mind as Harris put the shirt on, Mendoza said, "A few weeks on the trail muscles a man up. Takes the meat off his rump and puts it up above where it counts."

Frank buttoned the shirt and shoved the tail into his pants. "I got a long ways to go yet."

"You're getting there."

The horses in the remuda behaved themselves that day better than usual. It was a lazy day, and the scorching sun and choking dust seemed to ease up in the general indolence of the great, flat universe. Riding right flank, Harris managed to get a couple hours sleep in the saddle, dozing off briefly from time to time, as most of the others did.

That night the dark came cool and quiet, and feeling good, the men stayed up later than usual. Slim produced his harmonica and played it with relaxed pleasure, and Frank stretched out not far from the warm fire, listening to the talk going on around him.

Reece and Doc Bender were near him, and Reece said, "Thing I've been wondering about, Doc. Why'd you toss over a good job as town marshal?"

Bender folded his arms over his knees. "Oh, I don't know. Good pay, pretty easy work mostly. But I couldn't ever get used to shootin' a gun at somebody. Which is a thing I had to do every now and then."

Reece studied the ex-gunman carefully. "I'd say that was a good part of the answer. Not all of it."

A thin but genuine grin touched Bender's lips. "You thinkin' what a lot of others did? That I got scared?"

"No. Matter of fact, I'd lay heavy odds you didn't."

Bender picked a piece of cheat grass from under his legs and put it in his mouth. "You're right both times. I wasn't scared. And that wasn't the whole answer, exactly.

"Little while back I was making my midnight rounds in Wichita. Two fellows jumped me in the dark. Started out a fist fight. Then one of 'em started shooting." Bender's shoulders moved forward in a slow shrug. "Make a long story short, I killed them. Had to, before they killed me. Someone come runnin' with a light. Turned out they were both green kids. Guess they'd been looking for some excitement, got too much whisky in them.

"Next morning I turned in my badge and started look-

for a job. Being a lawman is no way to make a living."
Reece stared into the fire thoughtfully. At last he
lifted to his feet. "Better go take a look at the horses."
When he'd walked away, Frank mused over what
nder had said, and other snatches of conversation came
y to his ears.

Charley said, "Well, you dumb saddlebums won't be-
ve this, but that redhead I had back to Chicago really
ade me a proposition. She said, 'You stay here with
e, honey, and I'll take care of you the rest of my life.'"

Slim stopped playing his harmonica long enough to
y, "That so, Charley? What was she doin'? Lookin' for
first-class giggolo?"

"No, God damn it!" Charley couldn't think of a more
itable comeback, so he lapsed into silence.

Singer, who was rubbing his boots to a high shine with
handkerchief said, "Say, Joe, tell us about the time you
e them Indians."

"Oh, for Christ sake," Capper muttered. "Wish you'd
rget about that. Besides that, I never had but one Indian
my whole life, and then it was only a haunch. The way
u fellows carry on—"

"Did you have any salt and pepper, or did you take it
aight?"

"I'd just like to see you smart alecks starvin' to death
the middle of the winter some time!"

Peggy was washing dishes at the chuckwagon about
enty feet away from the fire, and Curtis had wandered
er for another cup of coffee.

Half drowsing, Frank was aware that Curtis was point-
g something out to Peggy underneath the wagon. A
oment later the cowboy reached under it with a stick
d Frank heard a faint whirring, like a boy running a
ck over a picket fence far away.

"You know," Curtis called. "You're as peaceful a pic-
re as I ever seen, sittin' there jabberin' away. Especially
u, Harris, layin' there like a bump on a log. Let's liven
e party up with a little visitor!" He flipped the stick
d a long, thick, ropelike object sailed toward Frank. It
nded half on and half off him. It was a big rattler, and

its mouth was open so wide with fury that Frank cou[ld]
have put his entire fist in it.

"Wow!" Frank rolled with terrified speed, dumpin[g]
the snake before its deadly fangs touched him. He slamme[d]
into Slim, who was squatting a little behind him, an[d]
knocked the harmonica flying.

As Slim got to his knees Singer stepped forward an[d]
kicked the rattler toward him. "Shoot him, Slim!"

Dodging quickly, Slim said, "Ain't my snake." He g[ot]
a poker from near the fire and flipped it toward Charle[y.]
"It's for you, Charley. It's a girl snake!"

"She's more your size, Slim. I like 'em that way, wit[h]
bigger hips!" Charley reached for a stick and flipped th[e]
writhing serpent toward where Slim and Singer wer[e]
standing together.

As Charley flipped the snake, Reece came into th[e]
circle of light and snapped, "Stop it!" But Charley didn[']t
hear him in time, and the snake was already arching dow[n]
toward the two men. Slim ducked aside, but Singer wasn['t]
fast enough. The rattler fell across his shoulder with writh[-]
ing fury and wrapped itself partially around his neck.

Singer screamed. He tore at the snake and flung i[t]
away. "He got me!" he cried in combined loathing an[d]
terror. "He got me in the neck!" With queer, panicke[d]
indecision, Singer ran twice in a small, erratic circle. The[n]
he ran out across the flats away from the fire, moaning[,]
"Oh, my God! My God!"

"Get him!" Reece yelled. He leaped the fire to take ou[t]
after Singer at a dead run, but Frank was already on hi[s]
way.

Singer was starting down a short embankment whe[n]
Frank jumped him from above and carried him to th[e]
ground. Before the nearly insane cowboy could squir[m]
away, Reece and Doc Bender were there to help pin hi[m]
down.

"I'll take his legs, Harris," Bender said. "You sit o[n]
his back."

Charley arrived a second later and helped to hold th[e]
flailing arms.

'Lie still!" Reece commanded. "You want to pump
it poison clear through you?"

Completely terrified, Singer rubbed his face in the
ad, twisting his head back and forth. "Oh leave me
ne," he wailed. "I'm goin' to die! I'm goin' to die!"

Peggy came running up with a lighted kerosene lamp
d held it so that Reece could examine Singer. Gripping
e cowboys head between his knees, Reece unclasped a
ife and ripped away the shirt. "Didn't get you on the
ck, Singer. Got you on top of the shoulder. You're
eding fast and clean. Must have hit a vein. If you'll
it up and sit still, maybe you'll make it."

Frank could see the cold sweat standing out on Singer's
oulders, and he knew that sweat was pouring down his
n face.

"Oh—oh—oh," Singer muttered, his voice thick with
kness and terror.

Reece slashed the skin deep at both points where the
gs had entered, and the hurt cowboy's body quivered
the additional shock. "Don't cut me," he pleaded.

"Cutting's all done." Reece returned the knife to his
cket.

"Bleed him good," Bender said. "Only way, after all
e running he did."

"Yeah." Reece squeezed around the wound with his
nds, forcing blood from the knife gashes. Then he
ned down and put his lips against the cuts to suck the
ison out. Mendoza had come in from the remuda and
d now, "You sure you want to do that, boss?"

Reece spit onto the ground beside him. "Don't want
do it at all. But it has to be done. Can't put a tourni-
et on top of a shoulder. No way I know."

When Reece finished working on the groaning man,
ey carried him back to camp and placed him near the
e, where they covered him with blankets.

Frank stood near the ashen-faced man, not knowing
at to do. The others, one by one, moved away. Soon
arris could hear them talking quietly, some of them over
sh cups of coffee.

"Hell," Reece was saying, "one of these first days, you'[re]
not going to be able to ride fifty miles around here wit[h]
out bumping into a fence. Way things are going, there'[ll]
be fences everywhere you turn. I'd rather fight India[n]
than cut through those damned things."

"So would Joe," Curtis joked. "He'd ruther fight I[n]
dians than most anythin'. Makes him hungry just thinki[n]
about it, don't it, Joe?"

"Oh, cut it out, Curtis!" Joe grumbled. "I was starvin[']
and I didn't even know the god-damned Indian! It wa[s]
nothin' personal. Besides, like I told you, I threw awa[y]
everythin' but one haunch."

Curtis laughed. "Which haunch you keep?"

"Well, the left one. Naturally. Right haunch is usuall[y]
tougher. Like your right arm is usually tougher."

Frank looked at them over Singer's now quiet bod[y]
and wondered what kind of men they were. Laughing[.]
joking. Making idle conversation. And right beside the[m]
a man lay seriously close to death.

Leaning down, Frank whispered, "Singer, there any[-]
thing I can get for you?"

Singer's eyes were closed now. His breathing was la-
bored and faint, and he didn't answer. The shoulder and
part of the neck were hideously swollen.

Frank sat down a short distance away and watched the
man. After a long time his breathing quieted down and
he seemed to go into a deep, peaceful sleep.

The vigil Frank kept was interrupted by Curtis. He
wandered over wordlessly and looked down at Singer.
Watching the man's eyes, Frank saw that he was looking
not at Singer's face, but at the cowboy's new boots. Curtis glanced up and his eyes met Frank's. They both understood in that moment what Curtis had come for. He
wanted to see if Singer was alive. He hoped not. He
wanted Singer's boots.

Frank's lips twisted with disgust.

Turning to the others, Curtis said, "I think old Singer's
dead."

Reece came over and felt for a pulse along the one hand

tside the blankets. Then he put his hand on the man's
est and over his mouth. He stood up and said, "Slim,
u and Capper and Harris get some shovels. Dig it deep.
n't want coyotes getting at him."

Reece moved away as Slim and Capper started for the
uckwagon to get shovels, and Frank followed them,
eechless at their casual indifference to Singer's death.

Slim handed him a shovel at the chuckwagon. "No rest
the wicked."

His voice slightly choked, Frank said, "How many tears
u think there'll be when they bury you, Slim?"

Not understanding the emotion behind the words,
m scratched his head. "Hell, I'll count myself lucky
anybody takes the time out to bury me."

Frank turned and saw Curtis, at Singer's body near the
e, taking off the dead cowboy's boots. He gripped the
ovel like a club and ran back to where Curtis now had
e first boot off and in his hand.

"Get away from there!"

"What?" Curtis demanded.

"Put that boot back on, you son of a bitch!" Frank
sed the shovel. "Put it back on him or I'll break your
ad!"

"You gone loco?" Curtis didn't move.

"You killed him! You started throwing that snake
und! Aren't you satisfied? You got to steal his boots
er he's dead?"

"I kilt 'im? You are loco!" Ignoring Frank, Curtis
nked off the second boot.

Trembling with rage, but unable to use the shovel
ainst the other man's bare hands, Frank dropped the
eapon, stepped forward and kicked Curtis in the side
the head. "How d'you like that boot, you bastard?"

As a crowd of cowboys gathered around them, Curtis
t to his feet and charged Frank. He was the shorter
an, but he was thick enough to outweigh Harris by
irty pounds. He bulled in with his arms outspread, took
punishing blow over the eye and kept on coming, throw-
g Frank back and down. Frank managed to get a knee

up as he went down, and the knee caught Curtis in t
groin. He grunted with pain and rolled away, and th
they were both on their feet again.

"That's enough!" Reece forced his way through t
circle of men around them and stood between ther
"What's the trouble?"

"This crazy kid walked up and kicked me in the fac
That's the trouble!"

"He was stealing Singer's boots!"

Frank was faintly heartened to hear a low murmur
resentment run through the men. It took him a whil
to realize that it was a false victory.

"Where do you get off, takin' them boots like that?
someone asked Curtis.

"Damn right," another agreed. "Who d'ya' think yo
are?"

"What we oughtta do," Capper said, "is play a littl
showdown. That's the only fair way t' decide who get
'em."

"You made me a lot of trouble, kid," Curtis growled
"I'm gonna bust you."

He charged Frank again. Frank had slugged him dur
ing his first charge without stopping him or slowing hin
down. Reece stepped in this time and punched him ir
much the same manner. But there was a difference. Cur
tis's head was rocked back and his forward lunge was
instantly switched into a backward flight. His feet left
the ground and for a brief moment he seemed to be sus-
pended in space at the end of Reece's fist. Then he
crashed to the earth and decided it would be a good idea
not to get up.

"I told you no more fighting," Reece said quietly. "Now
you three get busy with those shovels. Hasn't anyone got
any respect for the dead?"

Capper and Slim did most of the digging, Frank's
stomach churning. When they were down to about eye
level in the narrow trench, Slim said, "That oughtta do it."

Capper turned toward camp and yelled, "Okay. Bring
him on!"

They lowered the bootless man into the pit as far as

ey could by hand, then dropped him with a thump.
ece stood at the head of the grave. "Anybody know the
ht thing to say?"

"Not me," Slim murmured at Frank's side.

"Harris talks a lot," Curtis grumbled, "He could prob'ly
a speech."

After a short silence, Reece said, "All right. I'll do it."
e cleared his throat slightly. "Lord. When something
ppens like this, it's too damned bad. And people some-
nes ask how come it happened? Was it this fellow's
ult, or the other fellow's fault?" Reece glanced at Harris,
though he were talking to Frank and God at the same
ne. "Well, except in cases where it was out-and-out
liberate, it isn't for us to say. We don't know all the
swers. And we can't undo what's done, so that's that.

"I'll tell you this, Lord. There isn't a man among us who
n look at the two hands You gave him with the two
es You gave him, and really feel sorry for Singer. You
id a great thing for Singer, just like You've done a great
ing for all of us. You gave him, and us, life. You gave us
ands to work with and eyes to see. And we're in no
osition to complain about it, if You see fit to take back
hat You gave us. We have to allow that You know what
ou're doing. If it hadn't been a snake got him, it could
ave been a steer, or a Comanche, or a potgut hole on a
ark night.

"And I'll say this for Singer, Lord. He was a good man
ith cattle and horses, and he always did the best he knew
ow. I hope somebody can say as much for me when my
ime is up."

Reece stopped, and after a moment he put his hat back
n. "That's it. Fill 'er up."

Harris was the last to leave the lonely grave. He walked
lowly to the chuckwagon and placed his shovel on the
ailgate with the others. Beyond the wagon, there were
even or eight men gambling on a spread-out blanket near
he fire. They didn't use cards; someone had produced a
air of dice, and they were tossing for the things that had
elonged to Singer. His boots, wallet, gun and saddle.

That was about all there was left of the man. As Fra
watched from the wagon, Curtis blew on the dice an
threw.

"Got 'em!" he yelled gleefully. He stood up with th
boots and glanced over the fire with victorious arrogan
at Frank.

"Shootin' for his gun, now," Slim said. On his kne
beside the blanket, he rattled the dice intensely.

"Hey!" someone said. "Anybody ever get around
killin' that snake?"

"By God, I guess not."

"I'm puttin' a good hemp rope around me tonight."

"I've knowed snakes that's crawl ten miles to find
good hemp rope. Only way they got to scratch the
bellies."

Frank walked away from camp, out to a rock tha
jutted head-high out of the ground, beyond hearing di
tance of the others. He stood there quietly, lost in moros
thought.

There was no noise, but the feel of movement behin
him, and he turned.

Reece said, "Nice out here. Quiet. Almost makes yo
like Texas."

There was a silence, and then he said, "Harris, you're
not doing too bad. Better than I thought you would. Bu
there's more to being a good man on the trail than hav
ing a tough body. Whether you like it or not, you go
to have a tough mind, and a tough hide. Do you see what
I mean?"

"Yeah. I wish I didn't."

"This is kind of like a war, out here. Maybe you knew
somebody who was in the Civil War. Maybe your dad,
or somebody. Maybe they told you that you can't go to
pieces every time somebody got killed."

"That's a lot of maybes," Frank said tightly. "What
do they lead up to?"

Reece paused. "This is like a war out here, in a small
way. A war against the earth and the sky and longhorns.
You got to be strong to survive."

"Watching them shoot dice for Singer's stuff back

there—it made me think of getting my money and going
back to Chicago."

"Not all of them were in that game. Mendoza wasn't.
Doc Bender wasn't. I wasn't."

"Why should you be? You don't need those things he
had!" When the words were out, Frank was ashamed of
them.

After another silence, Reece said, "Tonight's the one
night I won't give you your money back. If you still think
you want it in the morning, you can have it."

He walked away, and Frank looked out across the end-
less, rolling shadows of prairie toward a sliver of moon in
the cloudy sky. The world was lonely and awfully big.
And standing beside that rock, he felt no larger than an
ant standing beside a pebble.

CHAPTER NINE

THE NEXT MORNING, Frank started to look for Reece. He found Mendoza building up the fire while the rest of the cowboys were yawningly pulling on boots and rolling up their beds. "You seen Reece?"

"Yeah. He went out to check the horses." The Spaniard looked up at Frank sharply. "You look like you didn't sleep so good."

"I didn't."

"You got troubles?" Mendoza spoke quietly, standing up beside the younger man.

"I'm quitting." The words came out in a strangled whisper.

"How come? What for?"

"Because damn near everyone in this outfit is an in-human son of a bitch who doesn't give a damn if the others live or die." Frank touched Mendoza's shoulder. "Not you. You know I don't mean you. But I can't stay with men I don't respect. Laughing and all while Singer was lyin' there dying. And Reece was the worst of the lot, because I expected more of him."

For the first time, Mendoza's eyes flared with anger. "You think Reece didn't care that one of his crew died?"

"He was sittin' there talking about fences!" Frank said bitterly. "He didn't care about anything!"

"Just one thing I want to tell you, kid." Mendoza spoke in a cold, harsh voice that he'd never used with Frank before. "He was sittin' there talking about fences, but he had two lives to worry about. Not just Singer's, but his own. You saw him suck that poison out of Singer. Well, yesterday morning his mare reared at a tumbleweed. She threw her head back and caught him in the face. His mouth was cut inside. It was bleeding. But he sucked as much poison out of Singer as he could, last night. And you say he don't care?" Mendoza turned toward the fire and kicked a log into better position to catch fire. "Go ahead and draw your time." He walked away.

Frank stood still for a moment, taking in what the Spaniard had said. Then he walked quickly after the other man and caught up with him. "Mendoza," he said. "I didn't know."

The Flying R crew moved on south into the dryest, most desolate country Frank had ever seen. Under the blasting heat of the sun, the flatlands stretched barren and lonely as far as a man could see, before his vision grew hazy in faraway shimmering heatwaves.

Two days beyond the solitary mound of earth they'd left behind, Frank pulled his gelding to a halt, waiting for the remuda to catch up with him. Doc Bender had gone on ahead to scout for some water. He now brought his horse back at an easy lope and pulled up beside Frank. "There's a creek down there." He nodded toward a distant flat. "Water's movin' in it. It's good."

"Enough to take a quick bath?"

" 'Fraid not."

Frank's attention was caught by a slight movement perhaps two hundred feet away. He squinted at the sagebrush where his attention had been caught, and an odd-looking, furry little animal with enormously oversized legs hopped into view.

"What's that?"

"Jack rabbit." Bender grinned. "Doesn't look like much of anything just now. It's only a baby."

Capper and Slim drew abreast of them, riding point on the remuda, and Slim pointed to the sky. "That fellow best hightail it for his hole."

Above them, a speck in the sky, a chickenhawk was soaring with motionless wings.

"It's comin' down," Capper said. "It's seen the rabbit. I bet two to one on the hawk."

Slim judged the distance between the tiny rabbit and its hole. "At them odds, I'll take the bet."

Frank glanced at the two cowboys. Their faces were expressionless as they watched the life-and-death drama unfolding before them. The hawk was plummeting si lently down now, its talons stretching out to clutch the baby rabbit.

The jack rabbit saw the onrushing bird of prey too late. It was obvious even to Frank that the little furry ball would never make it as it bounded with quick, ungainly leaps toward its hole.

The speeding hawk was only a few feet from the rabbit, and in the last instant a gun roared so near to Frank that his ears rang and his gelding sidestepped in fright. The hawk became a shapeless mass of feathers that hit the ground and rolled to a stop.

Doc Bender put his revolver back in its holster. "Sorry to spoil your fun, boys. Bets are off."

"What'd you have to go and do that for?" Capper complained.

"It's all right by me," Slim said. "Hell, it was worth it to see a shot like that."

Bender called to Reece and told him there was water ahead as the remuda and the chuckwagon came closer. Then he rode on alongside Frank.

"I guess that was a foolish thing I did," Doc said.

"I don't think it was. I think I kind of see the way you felt." Frank reined the gelding around an outcropping of rock and added, "Didn't think a six-gun could shoot that straight."

Bender studied him for a moment. "You learnin' to shoot the one you're wearing?"

"Haven't had much time. Only shot a few rounds out of it so far. You got any advice for a beginner?"

"Yeah. Leave it in your holster. You stick to your rifle. It'll do the shootin' jobs you want to do better, and you'll live longer." Bender squeezed his horse into a run to head off a mare wandering away from the others.

Three days later Mendoza raced back to the main body of horsemen after scouting along up ahead. He hauled his pony to a stomping halt and shouted happily. "I've seen Mexico! The Great River is in sight over the next hills!" He reined his mare into reaching distance of Frank

nd slapped him on the shoulder as some of the cowboys
ode ahead with delirious shouts of joy. "Now, my boy,
n Chihuahua you will learn truly how to live! There is
nusic and wine and women!"

Reece rode up as Mendoza finished. "You're barking
p the wrong tree, Mendoza. Harris is the only one of us
vho probably has a pretty girl waiting for him in Chi-
uahua."

"Huh?" Mendoza grunted, perplexed.

"Or was I misreading the look I saw you give Vidal's
laughter that night in the lobby?"

Frank said uncomfortably, "I didn't know you were
ooking at me looking at her."

"Cowman ain't worth a damn unless he's got eyes in
he back of his head." Reece turned to shout at the men
lriving the remuda. "Next stop Mexico! Keep 'em mov-
ng!"

CHAPTER TEN

CHIHUAHUA's dusty streets were lined with squat adobe buildings and countless animals, pigs, chickens and cows that wandered about as casually as the human citizens of the town. After making camp outside the city, all of Flying R but a skeleton crew rode into the town.

Frank was fascinated by the sights and sounds and smells of the place. Women seemed to be singing or screaming incessantly from behind the adobe walls. Guitars strummed within the cantinas they passed, and there was an air of gaiety and excitement everywhere.

"We're in luck," Mendoza told him as the riders moved at a walk into the center of town. "Must be a fiesta coming. I can feel it in the air."

"That's not what I wanna feel," Charley laughed. "Where's them Spanish señoritas?"

The streets in the center of Chihuahua were decorated with gaily colored streamers and festoons, and on a platform in the middle of the main square an orchestra was playing fast Latin rhythms.

"Boy, we damned well hit her right," Capper said. "Ain't seen a Mexican holiday in a coon's age."

"I'm going out to the Vidal ranch," Reece said, pulling his big black up short. "Like you to come with me, Mendoza. The rest of you can stay in town."

"I'd like to go with you," Frank told him.

"Okay, Harris. Thought you might." Reece hailed a passing man and asked directions in Spanish.

Mendoza translated the answer for Frank. "He says once you get out of town there is hardly anything but the Vidal ranch."

Turning to the others, Reece said, "Whatever you boys plan on doing, tonight's the time to do it. We'll be working our humps off tomorrow, trail-branding cattle. One

70

hing. No fights. That understood?" He pushed his horse
into a walk. "Let's go, Mendoza, Harris."

After a two-mile ride beyond the outskirts of Chihuahua, the three horsemen came to a large gate and turned
into it. "I hope," Mendoza said, "that Vidal wasn't lying
about the cattle. Be a long way to come for nothing."

"Those wires I sent from Kansas were to check on him,"
Reece said. "He's got plenty of good cows. Only thing
is hitting on a price, and if he's too high there's other
good stuff not far south." To Frank he added, "For a
man who claims to be some sort of a partner with me,
you're awful untalkative about this deal we're getting
into."

Mendoza caught Reece's eye and winked. "All those
weeks in the saddle have toughened him up. Made a
strong, silent man out of him. The kind women can't
say no to."

Frank started to reply, but realized he'd only get in
deeper and remained silent.

Beyond a row of tall trees they came to a large adobe
home. On a small patch of lawn forming a patio, Señor
Vidal was seated with a handsome Spanish man about
Frank's age. The younger Spaniard stood up as he saw
them approach, and Frank saw that his eyes were hard
and arrogant.

Turning in his chair, Vidal stood quickly and said,
"Señor Reece! This is a pleasure!" He saw Frank and
stiffened slightly.

"How are you, Vidal." Reece stepped out of saddle
and ground-reined his black. He shook Vidal's hand. "I
think you've met Mendoza. And this is Frank Harris."

"Welcome, gentlemen." Vidal bowed slightly toward
the other two as they dismounted. "I believe the young
Harris and I have spoken before. As I recall, he writes
poetry."

"He does?" Reece glanced at Frank with disbelief.

"I did at one time. I gave it up in favor of the cattle
business." Frank paid as little attention to Vidal as was
politely possible. His eyes were roving the patio, the cor-
ridors and windows of the hacienda in search of Maria.

There were two large, iron-grated doors that stood open onto the patio, and Maria stepped suddenly out of one of them, walking toward her father. She stopped short, surprised to see the other men. Then her hand flew to her mouth as she recognized Frank.

"Ah, Maria, come here," Vidal said, extending his hand. "This is Señor Reece, Señor Mendoza, and Señor Harris, whom you may recall from Chicago." He put his arm around the shocked, unhappy-looking girl. "And gentlemen, this is my daughter Maria, and her husband Manuel Arriega."

Frank's mind froze on Vidal's words, refusing to believe them. His mind repeated them again, and it was still hard to believe. He realized he had been smiling at Maria, and the smile was still on his face. He stopped the smile, and a moment later realized he'd also stopped breathing. He inhaled deeply and searched the girl's face for some word, some explanation. All he could see there was pain and sadness. His lips moved stiffly. "You're married?"

"Yes," Vidal said. "They were married only last week. They make a handsome couple, don't they?"

Arriega sensed some of the emotion between Frank and Maria. He stepped toward her, his hard face not completely masking his anger.

"Please," Vidal said smoothly, "won't you sit down? Would you care for something to drink?"

"No, thanks." Reece flicked a look at Harris. "We're here strictly as cattle buyers, and we're in a hurry. I thought we might go out and look over your beef."

"As you wish, of course." Vidal turned to his son-in-law. "Manuel, will you have horses saddled?"

Arriega nodded curtly and left the patio. Reece and Mendoza turned back to their horses, and Vidal moved with them.

Frank found that he was for a brief moment alone with Maria. There were bitter questions racing through his mind, but all he could say was, "Maria?"

Her large eyes were tortured and confused, but she said nothing. She took one small step toward him, and her father called from his short distance away. "This way, Señor Harris."

Maria turned and hurried into the house, and then Frank joined the others.

Both Vidal and Arriega went with the three cattlemen, and the five of them rode out to a far pasture that was thick with grazing cattle.

"Beautiful, eh?" Vidal said.

"Not bad," Reece shrugged. "How many head have you got?"

"Twenty-six, perhaps twenty-seven hundred. I realize that's too many for you to take north."

"If the price is right, I'll take them all."

"That's a big drive."

"I have a big crew. The best men ever wore out saddles."

"Would you like me to run a count? Find out the exact number?"

"Might as well find out."

The three Flying R men sat their horses on the hill while Vidal and Arriega rode down to direct the vaqueros. Slowly the milling mass of bawling cattle was herded toward a huge corral at one end of the large pasture, to be run through a chute and counted.

"How long is this going to take?" Frank demanded. "I may shoot Vidal if I have to listen to his oily talk much more!"

"Easy, boy," Mendoza soothed.

"One thing I gave you credit for," Reece said. "That was having a good, hard business head. Here you are, set up to maybe make a killing in beef, and all you can think of is a pretty girl. There's no place in the world hasn't got pretty girls."

"I was going to marry her!"

"Forget it. If I make the kind of deal I want, you'll wind up owning better than two hundred head of prime beef. There's no girl in the world worth that many cows." Reece pulled his black's head up. "Let's go help 'em count. I don't trust Vidal an awful lot."

As the other two rode toward the corral, Frank turned

to look back in the direction of the Vidal hacienda. He saw Maria, handsomely mounted on a palomino, canter into view upon the crest of the hill. A minute later he reined up beside her. "I thought you would wait for me, Maria."

"Didn't you get my letter, Frank?"

"Letter? No—I left Chicago the day after you did."

"Oh. I wrote you," she whispered. "To explain the whole thing." Her voice broke off in uncertainty. "I never expected to see you again, Frank."

"But why didn't you wait at least a little while? Why didn't you give me a chance?"

Maria looked below into the sloping pasture and wet her lips nervously. "Manuel is coming. He's seen us together. Please, Frank, you must leave now. I am not permitted to see you alone."

"I want to know why you didn't wait!"

Before Maria had a chance to answer there was the beat of galloping hoofs, and Arriega brought his horse to an angry halt near them.

"I must explain, Manuel," Maria said awkwardly, "that Mister Harris is a friend of mine from Chicago."

"And I must explain to you," Arriega hissed, "that you are my wife!" To Harris he said, "You will not see her alone again. I believe Señor Reece is waiting for you."

When the cattle had been run through the chute, the tally stood at twenty-five hundred and sixty-eight head.

"What do you think of them?" Vidal asked Reece. "Have you ever seen more prime beef? They're fattened up, strong enough for a long drive."

"They look pretty good."

Frank's mind wandered to Maria as the two men talked about prices. Intent on his own troubles, he absently poured tobacco into a cigarette paper and tamped it in before wetting the paper edge. He was half finished with the cigarette before Vidal's hateful voice penetrated to him once more.

"—the Feast of Santa Margarita. There will be many

games and much amusement. I hope you and your men will come."

"If we get the trail branding done in time, we'll do that."

Reece rode away from the corral, and Frank fell in with Mendoza beside him.

"You look worse than you did the day the mare almost killed you," Mendoza said. "And that's saying a lot."

"Yeah?"

"Will you quit bellyachin' about losing one girl?" Reece said impatiently. "You just got yourself something like two-hundred and twenty head of cattle."

"I did?"

"Oh, God," Reece grumbled. "I'll bet you didn't pay attention to one word said down there! Might just as well have left you back in Chicago!"

"You tried to!"

"It'll be to my everlasting dishonor that I weakened. You're no cowman. You're a God-damned lover!" Reece grunted with disgust. "And I've not forgot what old Vidal said about you writin' poetry. You're hardly fit to associate with honest men!"

His sorrow turning to rage, Frank said furiously, "How would you like a punch in the nose? And what about you and your opera? That's worse than poetry any day!"

"Mendoza," Reece said, "have you noticed how fickle the young men of today are? One minute their hearts are broken. The next minute, they've completely forgotten about their broken hearts and are looking for a fight." He sighed.

"Yes," Mendoza said. "It is very sad."

CHAPTER ELEVEN

BRANDING started early the next morning. Every steer and cow Vidal owned was marked with an elaborate brand on the right flank.

"Looks like they heated up the iron scroll out of a church window and burned it on," Frank said.

"They call that a *quien sabe* brand," Mendoza told him. "Doesn't mean anything, like a good Texas brand does. It's just pretty." He watched the chuckwagon roll over the hill toward where their new camp would be, near the pasture. Then he stepped out of saddle and picked up a stick and leveled a section of ground with his hand. "Come to think of it, you don't know much about brands, I guess."

"No." Frank got down beside him.

On one knee, Mendoza scratched a rough R into the ground, and drew two lines that looked to Frank like horns on the R. "That's the flying R. Wings on an R. See?"

"Yeah."

Mendoza scratched it out. "All kinds of things you can do with an R. Like this. An R on its side like this, or lying down, is a Lazy R. Kind of put feet on it like this, and it's the Running R. Put a curved line, like the rocker of a rocking chair, under it, and it's the Rocking R. Put a downward line in front of it, and it's the Slash R. Draw a level line in front of it, you got the Bar R. Always read a brand from left to right, from top to bottom and from the outside in, and that's all there is to it."

"What was that last thing you said?"

"About outside in?"

"That was part of it."

"Like if you got an R inside a circle, that's the Circle R. You got a dot inside a diamond, that's the Diamond Dot. Got it?"

A shout came from Slim who, with Capper and Charley, now had a small, hot fire going. "Irons are gettin' hot, Mendoza! Bring us some cows!"

In addition to Vidal's *quien sabe* brand, the cowboys began to stamp the Flying R mark on the left flank of every animal. Then, with a running iron that was nothing but a white-hot poker, they touched each cow's left ear twice, searing two small indentations.

Frank had never known hard work until now, he realized after a few minutes. The branding crews worked swiftly, and the other cowboys had to drive steers and cows near the fire, lasso them, get off and hogtie them. There was time for about one deep breath while the branders did their work, and then he had to untie the animal, herd it into the big corral and go back for more.

The first calf to go under the iron bawled loudly in terror and pain, and Frank took the time a little later to swing down from his horse in the corral and pat the youngster. "They tell me it won't hurt long," he said kindly.

The calf turned away from him and unleashed a one-legged kick that caught Frank just above the left knee and nearly knocked him down. With instinctive outrage, Frank aimed a return kick, but he missed as the calf leaped away and scuttled to the far side of the corral. "All right, you little bastard!" Frank yelled at him. "You can go to hell!"

Driving two steers into the fenced enclosure, Mendoza said, "Never try to outkick a cow or a horse. They got more legs than you have."

After four hours of back-breaking work, half the herd was branded. Frank's arms were heavy and his hands were raw from rope friction, but he was coming close to holding his own. He rarely missed with the lariat and he could throw a steer both by catching its off forehoof and pulling it up under the body, or by twisting the horns. His main trouble was bulldogging, throwing a loop over the squirming hind hoof, another over the forelegs, and hauling the whole thrashing mess into a compact, fairly motionless mass.

"If I have to hogtie many more of them beasts for you," Slim told him as he knelt on a steer's neck and burned its left ear, "I'm goin' to send you a bill for a day's wages."

"I think I got the idea now. Been twisting the loop the wrong way."

At noon the men ate in shifts, the work going on without stop.

Estimating the growing number of cattle in the corral against those in pasture, Reece took a drink of coffee and said, "Ought to have it whipped by nightfall. Been runnin' them through about four a minute."

Not far from camp, Capper rode after a big steer, his rope flashing around his head. He let fly the loop and his horse skidded to a hard, low-rumped halt. Capper's hand whipped the rope around the saddlehorn as the steer hit the end of the line. Instead of going to the steer, Capper got slowly off his horse and started looking around on the ground. "Hey, Stanton," he called to one of the branding crew near him. "Take over that steer, will you?" He found what he was looking for and walked slowly into camp. "After fifteen years on the hurricane deck," he muttered, "I ain't never been hurt. Near starved one time, but never got more than bumps and bruises."

Reece put his coffee cup down on the ground. "Finger?"

"Yep."

Frank's eyes went to Capper's right hand. Where the index finger had been, there was a short, bleeding stump. Capper opened the hurt hand, palm up. He was carrying the severed finger in it. "I'll miss the damned thing."

Reece finished his coffee. "Fix him up, Peggy." He mounted his horse and rode back to where the others were working.

Frank's stomach tilted dangerously, and he hoped his tanned face wouldn't show the sickness he felt. "How'd it happen?"

"Caught it somehow betwixt the rope and the horn." Capper sat down as Peggy came toward him. "Startin' to hurt, now."

"Well, Capper," Charley grinned, "that makes you a genuine vaquero. Accordin' to the Mexes, you ain't no real cowpoke till you lost at least one ropin' finger."

When Frank went to his horse to go back to work, he stared for a long moment at the pommel of his saddle. The tree of the horn was wrapped tightly with a flat strip of rawhide to keep the rope from wearing directly on the short, erect horn. It was a tough piece of equipment, and he could see that if a finger—or a hand—were inside the rope when a thousand-pound steer slammed against the end of it, the weaker human flesh would be cut almost as if with a blunt axe.

During the rest of the grueling day, he paid special attention to the pommel, and he was vaguely aware that his teeth were clenched each time the rope sizzled around the horn-protecting rawhide strip, or snapped viciously under the pressure of stopping a running steer. . . .

The sun was down and darkness was almost on them when the last branding iron seared through the fur and into the hide of the last steer, and when Reece slammed the corral gate on the final animal, he said, "Good day's work. Good enough that we can afford to lay over to-morrow for the wind up of the fiesta."

"That's good," Charley grinned. "The Flying R is doin' fine on its quota of beef. But I ain't begun to get my quota of Mexican girls!"

Midmorning of the following day, the crew rode to the outskirts of Chihuahua where a large field had been set up for the Mexican games. Crowds of gaily bloused and skirted women mixed with the men who wore tight-fitted pants and jackets, and wide sombreros rimmed with tiny, short hanging balls that bounced and bobbed as they walked.

"What the little balls on the hats for?" Frank asked Mendoza.

"Well," the Spaniard shrugged. "They keep the flies off your face if you shake your head enough. Also I guess they're supposed to be good-looking. I like the plain

Texas hat better." He crammed his own wide-brimmed Stetson down more firmly on his head to emphasize his words.

There was a corral at one end of the field, and near it a square of raised canvas shaded the chairs where town dignitaries were seated to watch the games. Frank stood in his stirrups and saw that Maria was there with her father and Arriega. Seeing her, Frank's throat became dry, and he had the feeling she'd noticed him already and her eyes were avoiding him. Not so Arriega. His coal-black eyes were glowering at Frank with open hatred.

"Señor Reece!" Vidal called, walking out from under the shading canvas.

With Reece leading the way, the Flying R rode slowly forward through the men and women and laughing children to the edge of the chairs.

"We're so happy you could make it," Vidal smiled. "Will you join me in the shade, Señor Reece?"

"No thanks." Reece glanced onto the field where a horse race between a dozen vaqueros was being run. "See you got your contests going already."

"Yes. Perhaps your men would like to take part in them."

"Up to them."

"I'm half horse an' half gunpowder," Charley said loudly, "an' I'll take them fellows on any time."

There was a murmur of agreement from the others, and Vidal said, "Our judge is the alcalde." He gestured toward a distinguished old man with a pointed white beard who was seated in the shade. "I'm sure you'll find his decisions fair."

Reece, Mendoza and Frank were the only men, aside from Doc Bender who moved alone to a small hill to watch, who did not join in some of the contests. Slim and Arnold tried their horses in a quarter-mile run, but a Mexican youth on a big strawberry roan stud beat them out.

Charley and two others tried their luck at a chicken-grabbing contest. The bird was buried, except for his neck and head, in loose dirt in the center of the field.

dea was to lean out of saddle at a full gallop and grab
he bird's head and pull him out of the ground.

With a shrill yell, Charley aimed his horse at the
quirming, indignant fowl and charged across the field.
He swooped down far enough as his mare rushed past the
ird, but his hand grabbed thin air as the chicken ducked
he clutching fingers.

"They got that damned thing trained," he complained
s he cantered back to the crew.

"Maybe it's a virgin chicken and saw you comin',"
Slim suggested.

"Ahh! Speakin' of girls!" Charley saw a plump young
irl in the crowd and swung down. "There's that one I met
rst night in town!"

The buxom señorita left the man she was with and
ame to Charley's side. "Sorry you meese," she said.

"I'll practice by grabbin' you." Charley put his arm
round her and she rolled out of his grasp with experienced
ase.

"Come on," she teased. "I want you to meet my
riend."

"Oh, no!" Charley grinned toward the scowling man
vaiting in the crowd. "From his looks, he doesn't wanna
neet me. Anyhow, it's you I'm interested in!"

A Mexican was the first to successfully grasp the
hicken's head and pull it free of the dirt around it, and
nother Chihuahuan won the lancing contest hands down
•y neatly picking up four out of five rubber balls laid
n a line on the ground as he galloped by. Charley tried
vith the lance, too, but he broke the slender weapon and
lmost unseated himself as he sped by the first ball.

"Mexicans are the best lancers in the world," Men-
loza told Frank. "Next to Comanches. Charley didn't
tand a chance against that fellow."

"Yeah," Reece agreed. "They could put a blade on the
nd of a lance and give you a first-class shave at a full
allop."

Frank paid little attention to them. His gaze wandered
ncessantly, without his willing it, to where Maria sat
vatching the games.

The alcalde stood and announced the coming contest. "Throwing knives will be next. A distance of fifty feet. Accuracy and depth of penetration are both to be counted."

Two men set up a large, painted bull's-eye made of thick wood at one side of the field, and several Mexicans lined up to enter the competition.

"Cards are stacked against us," Reece said. "Nobody in our crew can throw a knife worth a damn."

Curtis and Holly entered the line-up, and were given first turns. Curtis put his knife solidly into the wood, but far from the center. Holly's knife thumped against the target hilt-first.

The third thrower, a slight Mexican, flicked his arm in an expert swing and his blade went deep into the bull's-eye. As the crowd applauded, the second Mexican made an even better throw, hitting almost exactly dead center.

"Serves us right for playing against the house," Reece shrugged.

Doc Bender had left his horse ground-reined on the hill, and walked to a point where there was open land beyond the contestants. As the third Mexican's arm went back, Doc pulled his revolver.

The knife flashed toward the wooden board and Doc's gun roared above the noise of the crowd. There was a shrill, short zing of sound. The speeding knife leapt crazily in midair and spun wildly out of its path and to the ground. There was a moment of complete, unbelieving silence, and then the crowd roared with approval at Doc's magnificent marksmanship.

The next Mexican hesitated, then pulled his knife and let fly at the target. The heavy revolver boomed again and the knife blade was shattered in midair. Both the Mexicans and the Americans were amazed, and they yelled and clapped their hands for him to continue.

Bender hit the next two knives, missed with his fifth shot, and sent the knife flying far across the field with his last bullet.

Raising his hands for silence, the alcalde at last quieted

he applauding audience. He turned toward Bender and
aid, "Brilliant! Brilliant! I am an old man, and I've
ever seen such a display of fine shooting, señor. We ap-
reciate skill. I believe I speak for everyone in declaring
he entire contest a draw as of now."

The crowd yelled in agreement, and the Mexican
aqueros nodded, accepting the alcalde's judgment in
ood humor. "And now," the old man announced, "the
ist contest of the day. The Game of the Cattle!"

Several vaqueros were driving a snorting herd of big,
aw-boned longhorns into the corral, and Frank said,
"What they going to do?"

"Crazy game," Mendoza told him.

"Why?"

"People get killed playin' it." Mendoza pointed to
vhere half a dozen riders on stout horses were dragging
big, roped bull into the corral. "They get a killer bull,
n outlaw. They spend a couple hours tormenting him
o get him crazy mad. They paint his horns red, sort of
nake-believe blood, and turn him loose in a corral already
rowded with steers. Idea now is, for some lunatic to
ide in there and put a little ring around one of the bull's
iorns."

Curtis had moved up and was listening. "That ain't no
un. That's plain foolish."

"Hell," Charley grunted, "count me outa this one."

The alcalde stood again, and Frank saw that Arriega
vas next to the old man now.

"Don Manuel Arriega has asked me to formally chal-
enge anyone who wishes to compete against him. He
nakes this challenge as last year's champion, and in the
iame of his recent bride, Señora Maria Arriega."

Frank looked at Manuel and saw that the man's dark
yes were staring directly at him. He shifted his weight
n his horse, and Mendoza whispered, "Don't do it, boy."

There was a shrieking bawl of animal pain from the
:orral, and the crowd turned to see the mad bull lunge
>ack away from a gored steer as the other cattle plunged
ibout the crowded enclosure in thunderous panic.

"Horns are red for real, now," Reece muttered.

Arriega leaned down and spoke into the alcalde's ear and the old man called out, "Señor Arriega wonders i perhaps one of the young Americans would like to answe his challenge."

Frank's jaw tightened as Arriega stared pointedly a him again, a faint smile on his face. He raised his hand "I'll try it."

CHAPTER TWELVE

A POWERFUL, coal-black stud was led near the corral and Arriega walked toward it from the stand.

"He looks like a good man," Reece murmured thoughtfully.

Frank shot the cowman a look of surprised anger. "He looks like an overgrown kangaroo rat to me."

Tall and lithe, Arriega mounted his horse with easy grace and rode back a short distance toward the stands. The alcalde threw a small, white ring to him, and he trotted back to signal the gateman to open the corral.

"Ring's got to be put over the horn," Mendoza pointed out. "Can't possibly get it on by throwin' it."

Arriega rode through the gate and was instantly part of the surging mass of horns and wild-eyed steers, as the gate slammed shut behind him. The crowd cheered loudly as he took a small quirt from his saddle and whipped his way through the cattle toward an open spot in the center of the corral where the huge bull was stomping and pawing at the ground, bellowing its rage.

"He's got that horse trained to do half the work," Mendoza observed. "But like Reece says, he's still a good man."

Arriega rode superbly, ducking the flailing horns around him and guiding his horse in short, quick turns with his left hand and leg pressure. The black was used to close work with cattle, and it moved, sure-footed and fast, sometimes avoiding the cruel horns that loomed up from all sides without actual guidance from its rider.

Arriega quirted a speckled steer out of the way, bringing the small whip down hard across the animal's face, and was in the center clearing where the bull was moving in short, lunging runs. Seeing the man and horse, the great bull blew a thunderous snort from its wide nostrils, lowered its head and charged with deadly speed.

Arriega whipped his horse aside in a rearing whirl, and

the bull's horn grazed the black's flank as he crashed on by into the bawling steers. Blood ran from the gash as the black raced to the opposite end of the small clearing. Spinning around, the bull charged again. A plunging steer threw its hindquarters into the insane beast, slowing it slightly, and Arriega twisted his horse under him, leaned far out of the saddle and put the ring over the bull's horn as it lumbered by.

Over the shouting and cheering of the crowd, Mendoza said loudly, "He's still gotta get out!"

Now Arriega was heading for the gate, forcing and whipping his way through the confused tangle of scared steers. Charging after the horseman, the bull slammed into a wall of cattle. His attention diverted by the impact behind him, Arriega's eyes swung back, and in that instant his horse tripped and went down on its knees. The crowd screamed as the rider almost disappeared in the sea of hoofs and horns, and then the horse was up again and moving toward the gate.

The black leaped out of the gate and stood trembling as it slammed behind him. Arriega, as cool as ever, swung down to examine the hurt flank, then turned the horse over to a vaquero. Smiling, he walked through the wildly cheering crowd toward his seat beside Maria.

A small mob of Mexicans now surrounded the Flying R men, waving fistfuls of pesos. "Want to make bet?" one of them yelled. "Make bet he lose?"

Curtis said, "I'll go ten pesos, just for the hell of it."

"I'll take fifty," Slim grunted. He added, as a low-voiced afterthought, "But it's throwin' ten dollars away."

"Who wants another fifty pesos?" Capper asked the Mexicans.

One of the most insistent vaqueros kept pointing his finger at Frank and yelling in Spanish. All Frank could make out was one word.

"What's he talkin' about—'perder?'" he asked Mendoza.

"Perder means two things," the Spaniard said. "Means to lose, and it means to get ruined. I'm not sure which he thinks you're goin' to do. Prob'ly both." Turning with tight face to Frank, he said in a low, tense voice. "Remember when I told you to grab the saddlehorn? Your first day? It seems a long time ago."

"Yeah?"

"When you did that I was proud of you." Mendoza bit the words off sharply. "It took real strength to do what had to be done. To not give a damn what anyone else thought. Well, I'm telling you again. Back outa this. It was a fool trick to stick your neck out in the first place!"

Frank looked at Maria, who was watching him for the first time, her eyes wide with fright. "I can't back out!"

There was no way for Frank to know whether Reece had heard this low-toned conversation or not, but the cowman said above the others, "Say, is there anyone around here wants to make a worthwhile bet?"

Vidal, getting up from his chair on the stand, called over, "What do you say to a thousand American dollars, Señor Reece?" He held out one hand in mild and false apology. "But remember, this is a game Americans do not play so often."

"Okay. I got a thousand says an American can do it."

Frank heeled his mare forward. Passing Reece, he said, "Thanks for the confidence." He was a few feet away from the Flying R crew when Reece's voice caught him. "Whoa, Harris!"

"What do you want?" Frank turned in the saddle as Reece rode out to him.

"This thing's got kind of out of hand."

"What are you talking about?"

"Well—" Reece rubbed his chin— "I didn't mind you offerin' your dead body up as a sacrifice to poetic love. But now I've been sucked into layin' some money on the line, which I ain't aiming to lose. So I'm playin' this hand myself."

"You are not!" Frank glared at him. "You had plenty of chance to speak up before!"

"Didn't have my bet up before." Reece raised his arm to signal the alcalde. "I'm taking Harris's place!" he called.

"You're showin' off!" Frank's face was set in tight, livid

anger. "You're makin' them think I'm scared, that I couldn't do it!"

"You're not talking about them. You're talking about her. And I'll tell you a little secret, Harris. You couldn't do it." Reece reined over to the stand as the alcalde announced the substitution, adding, "Since the contestant will be Don Thomaso Reece, any person wishing to change his bets may do so."

Furiously Frank spurred back to Mendoza's side, certain in his shame and dishonor that everyone was laughing at him. "God, how I hate that show-off!" he told the Spaniard.

Mendoza hauled off from the horse's far side and Frank caught only a glimpse of the speeding fist before there was the harsh thud of knuckles against his face and he was sprawling off his horse to the ground.

Mendoza rode toward Reece. No one paid attention to Frank, and few even noticed him fall, for all eyes were on the cowman riding toward the corral with the second small ring in his hand.

Reece saw Mendoza coming and grinned. "You figurin' on holdin' my hand?"

"You can call it off. Give up the bets."

"Old Mother Mendoza. You ever know me to give up a thousand dollars without a battle?" Reece abruptly swung out of saddle and stood on the ground. "That black of mine is a good cowpony. But not used to that sort of a crowd in there." He picked up a short, clublike stick on the ground. "Think I'll leave him out here."

The cheering crowd became deathly silent as Reece walked on foot toward the corral gate.

"You crazy?" Mendoza cried.

"Open 'er up," Reece told the gateman.

The Mexican looked with stunned bewilderment toward the stand, hoping for a word from the alcalde, and Reece said sharply. "Open it!"

The gate swung out and Reece stepped inside, among the crushing hoofs and horns of the packed steers. An unbelieving gasp tore itself from the crowd, and then, as they watched the lone man impossibly fighting his way through the frightened, milling animals, they became silent once more.

Jabbing and clubbing with the stick in his hand, Reece forced a zigzag path through the dusty corral as the ground trembled beneath the weight of the swarming cattle. A flashing horn caught him from behind and he spun away instantly so that only his shirt, not his body, was torn. Two longhorns, pushed by the others, caught him between their heaving chests and nearly crushed him before he walloped one of them on the side of the head and broke away. Ducking, dodging and spinning with powerful, graceful precision, he fought his way at last to the center of the ring, where the bull first noticed him.

As the killer charged, Reece ducked behind a circling steer, moving out of danger as the bull pounded savagely into the steer, smashing it back against the others near it, leaving it with fatally deep gouges in its side.

Leaping out into the circle behind the now hesitant bull, Reece dropped his club, grabbed the animal's tail and twisted it hard. The bull bellowed with deafening rage and twisted around with the speed and agility of a great, thick cat.

Reece stood quite still as the huge beast lunged at him for the second time. Then, at the last possible instant, he stepped swiftly aside. The bull plowed into the wall of cattle again, and as it pulled back, tossing its great head with lunatic fury, Reece leaped onto its back. He seemed to hang there forever, a hand holding one twisting, lunging horn. Actually it was no more than two full seconds. The time it took him to remove Arriega's ring, throw it away and put his own ring on the horn. And then he threw himself off the enraged killer, ducking behind the nearest longhorn as the bull lunged after him. He was almost crushed as the red-horned beast crashed against the protecting longhorn, for the force of the charge knocked the steer back hard, catching Reece between its flank and a nearby steer's shoulder. Fighting for breath, Reece grabbed the uninjured steer's horns and held on while the terrified animal lunged halfway around the corral, carrying the cowman away from the bull and into the stream of milling cattle.

Gulping fresh air into his lungs, Reece at last dropped away from his hanging hold on the steer and forced a weaving, ducking path to the gate.

Mendoza himself swung it open and grabbed Reece as the gateman hastily closed it. "You hurt inside, boss?"

"No. Got my shirt torn, though."

The crowd had remained quiet through the entire thing. Now one person finally yelled a high-pitched "Maravilloso!" and the others, breaking out of their stunned silence, cheered wildly.

"I'll bet they can hear this racket back in Texas, boss," Mendoza grinned.

"Let's go collect our bets."

"Oh hell!" Mendoza grumbled. "I forgot to make any!"

On his way to the stand, several Mexican girls threw flowers at Reece, and the alcalde made a speech about the beauty of bravery. He ended it by saying, "Don Manuel Arriega wishes me to state that his championship is yours, Señor Reece. He will not try to better you."

"Didn't think he would," Slim commented.

Frank stared moodily from his horse at the happy crowd and the Flying R men collecting their bets. He didn't dare look toward Maria. He was still too ashamed of what had happened.

Reece stuck the money Vidal gave him in his pocket and remounted. Riding to the Flying R crew he said, "Your time is your own until tomorrow morning. Keep out of trouble. Anybody wants to join me for a drink at the closest cantina, come on."

The others rode after him toward the main part of town, whooping and hollering, but Harris stayed behind. He looked toward the stand where the alcalde and the others were leaving, hoping to see Maria once more. She was not there.

A little Mexican boy grabbed at his boot and tugged it, looking up at him.

"What you want, kid?"

The boy shook his head, not understanding English. "Señor 'Arris?"

Frank nodded and used his one workable word of Spanish. "Sí."

The boy handed him a piece of paper and disappeared in the crowd.

Frank opened the folded paper. It read, "Mission north of Chihuahua. Eight o'clock."

His throat tightened and his heart bounced higher in his chest as he folded the paper and put it into his pocket.

CHAPTER THIRTEEN

MARIA was there at eight o'clock. Frank had been waiting for an hour when she came into the small, deserted church from a side door and pulled back the veil she was wearing. "I had to say good-by to you in an honest way," she said simply.

"But Maria," Frank whispered, groping for words and taking her hands in his. "When I got your note, I thought it wouldn't have to be good-by. Isn't there some way—"

"No. There is no way."

"Why did you marry him?" The words burst out of Frank in an angry, hurt torrent. "You don't love him! I know by looking at you! By watching you when you're with him!"

Maria's gaze fell from Frank's face to the hands held between them. "You know Father was troubled about us in Chicago. As soon as we returned here, Manuel and I became betrothed." Her voice became a whisper. "In this country, Frank, you must understand that children have nothing to say about these things—"

"I don't understand anything except that I don't want to let you go!"

"Frank," she said firmly. "Listen to me! Did you ever wake up early in the morning with the world so clear and beautiful that you felt you could stop breathing and go on living within the sparkling beauty of that morning forever?" She shook her head. "But you can't do it, Frank. The sun moves higher. You have to breathe. Nothing can make that moment stand still." Maria reached up and gently, sadly touched Frank's cheek with her fingers. "Our moment is past. I'll treasure it, Frank. But it is past."

"Maria!" Frank said with soft desperation. He moved toward her, but she turned and went quickly to the door. Hesitating, she said, "Good-by," and then she was gone.

There was the sound of a light carriage moving away outside.

Slowly Frank walked down the aisle toward the main door.

Frank stopped at the first cantina in town. He hitched his mare to the rail outside and was almost to the door when Slim stepped out. Seeing Frank, he said, "Hey, Harris. Best not go in there."

"Leave me alone. Gonna get drunk." Frank started to brush by Slim, but the other man's hand caught his shoulder.

"You hear me? Don't go in there. Charley's askin' to get himself carved up."

"I'll go where I damn well want to!" What Slim had said about Charley slowly penetrated, and Frank said, "He need any help?"

"That's beside the point," said Slim. "Point is, if you get one of their knives across your stomach, you got a helluva problem holdin' yourself together."

"Well, I'm not running out on him."

Slim shrugged and climbed onto his horse. "You're a good buddy," he said sardonically. He cantered down the street and out of town.

Frank pushed through the doors and went into the crowded, smoky room. He crossed the hard-packed dirt floor to the small bar on his left and said to the bartender, "Whisky."

"Tequila?"

"Whisky."

"Tequila?"

"Okay, tequila."

With the drink in his hand, Frank turned around to study the room. Through the thick, gray smoke hazing across the room, he saw Charley at a table in one corner. The cowboy hadn't seen him. He had eyes only for the plump señorita he'd spoken to at the games. She was sitting on his lap, running her chubby fingers through his hair. Charley had one arm around her, and a bottle in his free hand.

Down the bar from Frank was the girl's Mexican boy friend. There were three other men with him, and the foursome was staring with stern hostility at the amorous American.

After his second drink, Frank began to shoulder through the room toward Charley. Halfway to the cowboy, he found his way blocked by two of the hard-faced Mexicans. The other two came up behind him and he felt the sharp point of a knife jab uncomfortably into his back. One of the men in front of him nodded toward the door. He didn't move, and the knife in his back stabbed forward hard enough to bring to his mind more clearly than he'd ever realized it before that a knife can kill a man. A light sweat, not so much of fear as of sheer, horrible realization, formed on Frank's forehead. He turned slowly and walked toward the door. As soon as he was outside, two of the four men took out guns, and one of them waved his gun toward Frank's horse. Another unhitched the animal.

Frank mounted the mare, and as soon as he was in leather, one of the Mexicans slapped the horse hard with the open palm of his hand. Startled, the mare took off at a gallop.

Pulling up at the end of the street, Frank looked back and saw the four men still standing there watching him. Running seemed a cowardly thing to do, but he couldn't fight all of them. Only one thing to do. Get help. He pushed the mare into a rapid gallop toward the Flying R camp. . . .

The campfire was already dying down when Frank brought his mount to a fast, prancing halt, jumped off and ran into the dim circle of light thrown by the coals and occasional flickers of flame.

Joe Capper was bedded down close to the fire, and Frank shook him roughly. "Joe! Come on! Charley's in trouble!"

"Huh?" Capper sat up and looked bewildered.

Slim and Curtis were awake now, and Frank stepped quickly toward them. "You too! Charley needs help bad!"

"I told you to stay outta there," Slim yawned. Turning to Curtis, he shook his head. "Charley's stealin' some Mexican's woman."

Curtis blinked thoughtfully at the dying campfire. "No reason for me to get hurt, is there?"

"No!" Frank cried. "There's no reason for you to get hurt! Just a thing called loyalty that you never heard of!" His eyes fell on Doc Bender, who had been awakened by the noise. "Doc!" He crossed to Bender's side. "Doc, Charley's going to be killed if no one helps him. There's at least four Mexicans ready to jump him in a saloon!"

"Four of 'em, huh?" Bender said quietly.

"That's right." He added with growing despair, "What do you say, Doc?"

"I don't like the odds. Why are they sore at Charley?" Bender made no move to get up.

"Does it matter?" Frank backed away from them, disgusted and sick inside. "I thought you were his friends!"

"Where I come from," Slim said, "if a man picks a fight, he's gotta plan on fightin' it."

Reece's voice came unexpectedly from behind Frank. "Okay, Harris. Everybody's heard about Charley. Twice. Now will you shut up and go to bed?"

Frank turned toward the cowman and said flatly, "What are you going to do about Charley?"

"Same as you. Nothin'."

"They may be cutting him up back there right now!" Complete fury almost strangled Frank's words in his throat. "And all of you stay here without raising a hand to help him! How can you stand yourselves?"

"Get this straight!" Reece growled. "There's a herd of cows out there that means more to every man here than Charley's romance with some Mexican chippy! Those cows are wages and profits and life and death! They're worth more than any one man here and Charley knows it!"

Turning to include every man in his words, Frank said bitterly, "You're the most miserable bunch I ever saw in my life!"

"Nobody cares what you think!" Reece put his hands on his hips and said with calm authority, "Thing is, nobody's going to town to start more trouble and most likely get the whole population on our necks."

"Well, I'm leaving!" Frank faced the other men. "If Charley has any friends in this outfit they'll come with me. Otherwise I'll go back alone!"

"Nobody's goin' any place," Reece repeated, his voice dangerously low.

"I am." Frank turned his back on Reece and walked quickly toward his horse.

"Harris!" Reece said angrily. When Frank didn't stop, the cowman reached down and grabbed a crowbar from near the chuckwagon. He threw it and the spinning iron bar hummed across the camp and slammed into the back of Frank's knees. Before Frank could get up, Reece was on him.

Harris threw a wild blow that grazed the cowman's cheek, and he got a walloping punch on the jaw that bounced his head against the ground. Twisting with all the furious strength he could gather, Frank pushed Reece away briefly and tried to roll out from under him. The roll brought them close to the fire, with Reece still on top.

The cowman had the crowbar now, and with it in his hands he forced Frank's head toward the coals.

"Reece!" Frank gasped. "Look out—the fire!"

"I see it, boy!" With steady, brute strength, Reece forced Frank's head still closer. "Had enough?"

"No!" Frank gritted his teeth grimly.

The crowbar moved another inch.

The heat was searing Frank's face, and still the crowbar moved. "Enough!" he yelled. "I've had enough!"

His voice lowered to a hard whisper that only Frank could hear, Reece said, "While we're havin' this friendly little talk, there's another thing I'd like you to say."

"All—all right," Frank muttered hoarsely. "I'll say it!"

"Repeat after me—loyalty is the most precious thing on earth."

"Loy—loyalty is the most precious thing on earth."
Frank closed his eyes tightly. "My face is burnin'!"

"I will never waste it foolishly." Reece spoke with unhurried calm.

"I will—I will never waste it foolishly!" Frank's words
spilled out one over the other.

"All right." Reece got up, pulling Frank with him, and
gave Frank a final shove that sent him flying away from
the fire and onto the ground, where he lay panting. To
the other men who had gathered in various states of undress to watch the battle, he said, "Now let's get some
God-damned sleep around here!"

Turning from where he lay on the ground, Frank
panted harshly, "You don't even fight fair!"

"Sonny, in case nobody's told you yet, your schooldays
are over."

Frank shook his head. "Okay. I'll play your rules. I'll
be tough. And don't fight me again, 'cause next time I'll
use a crowbar myself."

Reece nodded, his face hard and expressionless. "You
do that, son."

CHAPTER FOURTEEN

BOOST 'EM!"

"Pinch 'em in up front or they'll be scattered all over hell's half acre!"

"Catch them stragglers on the flank!"

With the mighty noise of hard, rolling thunder, the herd moved north from Chihuahua at a shuffling trot. Once the pasture laziness was taken out of the steers, the cowboys settled them down to a steady walk, pointing them north toward the Rio Grande.

When Frank had first wakened from a restless sleep he saw that Charley had come in some time during the night. He was sitting by the fire, his left arm in a sling, his right hand holding a cup of strong black coffee. Frank got some beans from Peggy and went to the fire to take the morning chill out of him while he ate.

"Saw you wanderin' around in the cantina last night," Charley said. "Why'ncha come over? She had a sister."

"Nobody but a damn fool would get himself in a spot like that," Frank said roughly. He nodded at the sling and the blood-soaked bandage he could now see under it. "You got what you deserved."

The first few days showed Frank that the trip south had been nothing compared to actual trail driving. This was hard, constant, raw work that never slackened its demands on a man. In addition to the never-ending strain of twelve long hours a day in the saddle, shifts of night riding were doubled and tripled if the weather was bad. And the weather was never good. One blistering hot day, riding drag, Frank figured out that there were more than ten thousand hoofs moving up ahead of him, and every one of them was kicking hot, choking, strangling dust straight into his face. The handkerchief drawn up around his nose and mouth was so covered with dust that it didn't look like cloth, but more like a board made out of dirt, and his eyes were swollen and red from the thick clouds of sun-hazed dust swelling around him.

Another time it rained three days in a row. Ankle-deep and fetlock-deep mud was one thing; this was another. His gelding at times went nearly knee-deep in the mucky sea of mud left by the thousands of hoofs ahead. Now, too, he learned how truly, completely and horribly stupid cattle were. Half a dozen steers slipped and fell in the mud and were trampled to death by the others before they could regain their footing. The cows behind came on dumbly, plodding, and walked over the downed animals as though a fallen body were only a slight rise in the ground. Several steers, faces lowered into the driving rain, walked over a slanting embankment and rolled to the bottom of the shallow ravine, and every other cow on the flank behind them would have followed if Reece hadn't forced his horse along the edge of the ravine, yelling and beating them to safety with a twirling lariat. The ravine was closed at both ends, and the cowboys had to haul the dumb creatures out of the muddy pocket with ropes. One steer managed to break a leg. Slim cut its throat, not daring to shoot it for fear of setting off the already spooky herd moving by. "We'll be eatin' beef again tonight," he grumbled. "Bacon an' beans an' beef! Sometimes I'd like to live on a island an' eat nothin' but peanuts and bananas for the rest of my life!"

On the third night of the storm, Frank was riding graveyard with Mendoza. The Spaniard had gradually settled back into his easy friendship toward Frank, but he rarely gave advice any more. On Frank's part, he had ceased being friends with anyone. From the night of his fight with Reece he'd built up a cold, hard wall around him that started with telling Charley he'd gotten what he deserved.

As Frank passed Mendoza, the resting herd was sleeping with fair calm in the dark mud and drizzle of night, and somewhere in the middle of the drowsing mass a calf bawled with mild unhappiness. There was a distant roll of thunder, and an almost electric magnetism filled the still, wet air.

"How's it go?" Mendoza called softly.

"All right." Frank swung in the saddle to stare through the dark and reaffirm his own statement. Then he said with low-voiced amazement, "My God, look at that!"

Far out in the herd a steer was standing among the others lying around him. His outline was only the dimmest of shadows. But playing around his head was a waving, bouncing ball of blue fire.

Curtis, on the far side of the herd, had seen the mysterious, flaming ball too, and as it turned orange, he started to slowly sing, "Oh, blue grow the lilacs, blue grow the lilacs, and blue is the girl I left behind me with a child—"

"That's St. Elmo's Fire," Mendoza said softly. "Plays around on a steer's horns sometimes. He can't see it. But if one of the others does, those beefs may take off like a shot." He rode on, joining Curtis in the slow, soothing song about the pregnant girl left behind in "San Antone."

Moving around the herd, Frank sang too, filling in the words he didn't know with words made up on the spur of the moment. The cattle, once their ears were hooked onto the calm, safe-sounding voices trailing through the air, were generally too stupid to pay attention to anything else. The eerily glowing ball of fire disintegrated into nothingness without spooking the animals, and the rest of the night was peaceful, except for the time when the lead steer took a notion suddenly to go swimming in a spur of the Rio Conchos nearby. Frank rode knee-deep into the swollen river to herd the bell-cow and several followers back onto the muddy ground. Shivering from the cold, he muttered, "And that hollow-headed brute's our lead. The one steer that's supposed to have an ounce of sense!"

The days and nights of grueling work, Frank realized, were good for him in one way. There wasn't time to think about Maria. When he rolled up at night, he'd sometimes remember her with painful clarity. The way she'd looked at him in the church. The one, wonderful evening they'd had alone together in Chicago. These thoughts would pound at him with bittersweet sadness and torment him with what might have been. And he'd turn and toss and worry the memory around before the tiredness in his bones drugged him to sleep.

Reece and Mendoza were sitting their horses on a rise beyond the Rio Grande one day, and they watched Frank far away and below as he pushed his mare into an effortless canter and expertly quartered across a flat and into a hollow to drive half a dozen hidden strays back into the herd.

"He handles that cayuse like it was part of him," Mendoza said. "He'll make a top hand."

Reece nodded silently. When Frank rode up the flank to haw some cows in that were bulging too far out in the line, Reece said, "You think I been too rough on him, don't you."

Mendoza scratched his neck and shrugged. "There never was a man harder on me than my big brother. Did me good. But you're even harder on him. Putting him drag nine times outa ten. Putting him on right flank every time we cross a river. Putting him on stray roundup every time we hit broken country."

"I'll say one thing for me, Mother Mendoza. At least I never knocked him off his horse."

Just short of the Pecos, Frank rode out on his own after strays. He was finding that the toughness in him was a thing of strength. As long as he kept the stiff, unyielding hardness inside him, he could do everything Reece ordered, and do work on his own besides. He was part owner of this herd, and he was going to see to it that the herd got through to the Wichita sidings, even though he had only the vaguest idea of the direction of Wichita. He found a newborn calf huddled beside a dead cow not far from camp, and he rode to the top of a hill and yelled at the nearest man. "Capper! Come here!"

Capper rode down into the draw where Frank was hoisting the calf to his shoulder. "What you want?"

Frank tossed the baby over Capper's saddle in front of

the man, and Joe yelled, "Hey! Get him off there! He's
still wet!"

"Take the calf back to the herd and find a cow that'll
feed him."

"To hell with that! Leave him for the coyotes!"

"Do what I said," Frank ordered.

"But he's a sticky mess!"

"He's worth ten dollars in Chicago. What are you
worth in Chicago?"

Capper was getting close to a fighting mood, and Frank
wasn't going to budge. Reece's voice came from behind
them. "He's right, Joe. Take him down to the herd."

When the muttering cowboy rode out of sight, Reece
took time to light a cigar. "Glad to see you're learning."

Frank turned a cold eye on him. "Yeah, I'm learning.
I've learned a cow's more important than a man." He
walked to his horse and swung up.

"Say, Harris." Reece held his cigar in his hand and eyed
the end of it with idle speculation. "You think much
these days about that girl back in Chihuahua?"

"Some."

"You know, that deal wouldn't have worked in the
long run. It's none of my business, but you're better out
of it."

"What you said in the middle was right. It's none of
your business." Harris rode up out of the draw and away.

Reece rode to the top of the draw; his eyes stern with
anger. He glowered at the immense herd strung out across
the prairie to his left. Removing the cigar once more from
his clenched teeth, he waved the smoke in a sweeping
command and roared, "All right! Drag up, there behind!
Keep 'em rollin'!"

It was that night that Frank rode the herd until midnight and then passed the shadowy horseman on his way
to camp. It was a cloudy, black night, and he'd recognized Slim, who came to replace him, only by the man's
voice.

Circling the herd toward the speck of a campfire in the
distance, he heard the whispered tinkle of metal on metal.

It was louder than the faint bouncing of a bridle chain or the tiny ring of spurs. He felt more than he saw the blurred outline of a rider a little distance away, and he said, "Mendoza?"

The outline melted away and the whispered tinkle could be heard no more.

When he got to camp, the first man he saw at the glowing fire was Mendoza with a half-gone cup of coffee in his hands. "How in hell did you get back here so fast? And why don't you talk when you're spoken to?"

"Huh?" The Spaniard looked puzzled.

"I passed you coming in."

"No you didn't."

"Well, I sure passed somebody. And this ain't the most crowded part of the world."

"Could you see him at all?" Reece asked quietly.

"No. Wouldn't have known he was there, except I heard a kind of tinkle. Wouldn't have heard that if it hadn't been for one of those short, quiet times when a cow isn't mooing, or anything, and you can almost hear yourself think."

"Not much jayhawkin' goin' on these days," Curtis said from where he sat near Reece. "Besides, we're four or five hundred miles too far south."

"From what Frank says," Mendoza put in soberly, "might've been metal beads, or bracelets, makin' that little tinkle."

Reece nodded. "Double the guard on the graveyard shift, Mendoza."

"You mean Comanches?" Frank said. "That was a Comanche?"

No one bothered answering.

CHAPTER FIFTEEN

IT WAS late morning of the next day when Frank saw five distant dots of horsemen. He was riding drag, as was usual through the dusty country, and he squinted through eyes inured to the hard sun and boiling dust and saw the riders briefly specked against the top of a rise to the west. They were moving at an easy, unhurried pace, parallel to the herd.

Frank shouted to Curtis, "Hold their rumps down for me for a minute!" and rode out of the drag to abreast of Reece on the right flank.

"You see those riders over west?"

Reece nodded, but said nothing.

"Ain't you curious about 'em?" ·

"I know everything about 'em I want to know."

"What are they?" Frank asked with obvious disbelief.

"Comanches," Reece grunted. "After spare strays."

Frank turned and squinted hard into the distance, but the horsemen were still unrecognizable dots. "How can you tell?" he demanded. "And how d'you know what they're after?"

"I know what they're after because stealin' cows is one of their basic rules of economics. I know they're Indians 'cause they're riding single file and keeping their mouths shut." Reece turned to Harris beside him and gave him a frowning glance. "It's white men who insist on riding together and jabbering their fool heads off."

At dusk they came to a wide, dry, river bed where sloping walls eased down some twenty feet to the flat bottom. The river bed slanted down from faraway hills to the north and broke off about a mile south into a

104

azy pattern of ravines and gulleys where the flats be-
me wild, chopped-up country.

"Bed 'em in the wash," Reece decided. "Easier to keep
em from being stampeded or stolen."

Mendoza nodded agreement, and Reece raised his
oice. "Okay, boys. We'll put 'em in the gully for tonight.
nd those of you ridin' night herd—anybody lets some
eers wander down into that rough land to the south will
nswer to me! It'd take a lifetime to find 'em in that
gsaw puzzle."

With the first light of morning, Reece got up and
ulled on his boots and went over to the fire. Peggy and
Mendoza were already eating beans and bacon from a
ve-gallon pail simmering on a screen over the fire, and
e said, "Mornin', Peg, Mendoza. That was the first
eaceful night's sleep I had since we left Chihuahua.
)idn't expect it."

Peggy ladled him a plate of breakfast. "Not all that
eaceful."

"What happened?" He glanced sharply at them.

"Nothin' much." Mendoza ran his tongue over paper
s he finished building a cigarette. "About forty head
andered off all in a lump. You'd think them particular
rty was all related or somethin', way they took off." He
t the cigarette with a burning branch of sagebrush from
he fire. "They'll be back."

"Who went after 'em?"

"Harris."

"Harris? Harris, by himself?" Reece put the food down
nd looked hard at Mendoza. "You shouldn't have sent
im out alone. You know there's Comanches around."

"I didn't send him. He told me he was goin' and he
vent."

Reece picked the beans back up and jabbed his spoon
t them. Then he said, "How long ago?"

"Couple hours before daylight."

"Which way?"

"South."

The camp was up, finishing breakfast, and the full ligh of day had preceded the sun, when Doc Bender strolle to a high spot just out of camp. His voice came dow into the camp a moment later, calm and relaxed, bu there was something in it that made every man turn toward him. "Reece. Come 'ere."

The entire Flying R crew moved toward the rise wher Bender was, and Curtis yelped, "Comanches! Must b every Comanche in Texas out there."

"I make 'em about thirty or thirty-five," Doc said "War party."

The advancing warriors were still nearly two mile away, to the south and east, and they were heade straight toward the herd, at a fine angle away from th camp.

"They want the beef more'n they want us," Reec said. "Get your rifles. We got a job on our hands holdin the herd and them too." As the others dashed back t camp, Peggy, Doc and Mendoza, who already had the long guns, stayed on the hill with Reece.

"I preferred the Comanche fifteen years ago," Pegg grumbled, "when they din't have but lances and arrow Half them fellows is carryin' guns."

"Just look at 'em!" Reece's head nodded in admiratio "The finest light cavalry in the world!"

Doc had been studying the land before the approach ing Indians carefully. Now he picked up a pinch of dus and tossed it into the air as the morning sun's rays brok over the low hills to the east. "From the scrub oak leave and dust, I'd make it about two yards right windage whe they get in rifle range," he told the others.

"I been countin'," Curtis said. "There's thirty-two Don't it make you kinda' hungry, Joe?"

"Shut up!" Capper growled nervously.

The Comanches, still far away, broke from an easy smooth lope into a deadly swift gallop now that brough them curving gracefully in a wide arc to the edge of th river bed a mile south.

Most of the men had taken shelter behind rocks an

shallows about the hill. Mendoza had scrambled down
nto the river bed to warn the riders on the herd, and now
e ran to the hill as Curtis raised his rifle for a long shot,
elling, "Look at 'em come!"

"Don't waste it!" Reece ordered. "You couldn't hit a
arn at this range."

"Ahh!" Curtis lowered the rifle. "I was just tryin' to
et a little supper for Joe."

Suddenly the Comanche chief, astride a clean-limbed
into, brought his pony to a dancing halt and raised his
and to stop the others.

"Wonder what's up?" Bender muttered.

The Indians grouped loosely at the edge of the river
ed as their leader pointed at something ahead of them
1 the wash. Whatever it was, it was invisible to the cow-
oys on the hill.

"What'd they stop headin' this way for?" Slim de-
anded of no one special, his voice brittle with tension.

"They're after something else." Reece frowned un-
asily as the Comanches disappeared, riding swiftly down
ito the wash. "Only one thing it could be. Harris is
own there with that bunch of strays."

"So they're passin' us up?" Curtis said hopefully.

"Sure. Better deal down there. Kill one man an' they
et forty head of cattle." Reece walked down the hill a
ew steps and tilted his hat thoughtfully, staring at the
lace where the Comanches had disappeared.

Doc Bender shook his head grimly. "We can't go down
here after the savages. Be outnumbered in broken-up
ghtin' nearly two to one."

"Best odds we could hope for," Mendoza agreed.
Have to leave some men with the cattle."

"Well hell," Curtis said loudly. "No question what to
lo! While they're busy with Harris and his steers we can
et outa here! Let's go!"

Reece whirled about and said with sharp command,
'Mendoza! We're gonna stampede the herd down that
iver bed!"

"What?" the Spaniard shouted. "I like the kid too,

but you'll never comb the herd outa that country at th end of the arroyo!"

"It's my herd!" Reece ran down the hill toward cam and swung onto his black. "Come on!" With the othe trailing quickly behind him, he galloped along the edg of the wash and yelled to the men on the low flank, "G outa the way!"

With Mendoza and Bender galloping close behin him, he raced his black headlong down the wash at th north edge of the herd. "All right! Stampede!" he roare pulling his gun and blasting the still morning air. "Ru damn you, run!" Charging his black straight at the su denly terrified cattle, he added a mighty, ear-splittin "Yaaahhooowaahhh!" to the pounding blasts of his gu

Doc was shooting so fast to Reece's right that th bullets sounded like one, long roar, and Mendoza w screaming wildly at his left, whirling his lariat in a swif hissing circle.

The cattle broke loose with a great, earth-shaking ro of hoofs, and thundered in a horrified, horrible, speedin crushing mass down the wide arroyo.

Frank heard the Indians before he saw them. Ther was a dim, rhythmic pounding that came to his ears ov the shuffle of the steers he'd rounded up, and when h turned around, he caught a glimpse of the leader a lon rifle shot behind him.

"Move!" He hauled out his lariat and slapped th rumps of the steers walking before him, urging them int a mild, stiff-legged run that was little more than a tro Afraid to push them harder for fear of setting off th main body of cattle ahead, he rolled his rope now, an put it back in the saddle loop, calling firmly to the steer "Hah! Hike on!"

Turning for another look, he saw what seemed to b a fair-sized army of Comanches now, and they were gai ing swiftly. "Go! Hah! Skin out!" he called to the steer They would have to make it under their own steam now

Frank whirled his mare to the left side of the arroyo where a clutter of fallen rocks afforded protection. He jerked his rifle out of the saddle holster and threw a fresh shell into the breach. Then he waited for the Indians to come around a slight bend in the arroyo.

The chief rounded the bend and Frank could see him clearly at this distance, a nearly naked man with beads around his neck, a rifle in one hand and a buffalo horn warbonnet on his head. Frank swung his rifle toward the Comanche, aiming over the rock before him, and the chief saw the slight movement, automatically raising his own gun as he sped forward.

Neither fired.

The Comanche suddenly slammed his pinto to a halt and wheeled uncertainly. At the same moment, Frank felt and then heard, the earthquake behind him. The walls of the river bed actually trembled under the immense power of thousands of tons of rushing steers. A few pebbles were shaken loose at Frank's side and rolled down the incline near him.

As the growing rumble swelled to hideous thunder, Frank ignored the hesitating Comanches and started to pull his mare's reins, dragging her out of the arroyo. She clawed her way up the steep bank and stood panting as Frank ducked back to the river edge.

His forty strays came by first, running as though hell were sitting on their rumps, and a few yards behind them was a solid, speeding wall of terrified steers.

The Comanches had scattered, but not all of them made it. As Frank watched, the swift, cumbersome sea of steers caught two braves in a shallow pocket in the wall at the far side of the arroyo. The Indians had evidently hoped to sit it out there, but the bulging mass of cattle swarmed up and into the pocket. Both riders went down, and one of the horses. The second horse managed to stay on its feet in the crush and Frank last saw him running around the bend with the herd. Another Comanche was killed as he tried to run his horse up a steep incline. The ground gave way. The horse rolled back down the slope, spilling his owner, and they both went under the hoofs.

Still another warrior suddenly appeared, riding up the slope at an angle and almost straight toward Frank. Frank wet his lips, raised his rifle and fired. He saw the brave fly backward off his horse, but he closed his eyes briefly rather than watch the rolling tumble to the spiked ocean of rushing horns below.

Reece was riding drag on the steers' rumps so closely that he was almost part of the stampede. Frank saw him below, and then at least a hundred more straggling steers went by. The cowman had reloaded during his wild ride down the arroyo, and a moment after he saw Frank at the top of the slope, he saw the bonneted Comanche, who had somehow escaped the steers. The chief was afoot. He raised his rifle toward Reece, and Reece shot him.

A warrior who had been caught in the rocks lining one wall was injured but not dead. He fired at Reece and the cowman felt a numbing shock spread through his right leg. Both he and Harris cut loose at the Indian and he slumped over dead, his dropped rifle clattering on a rock a few feet below.

His eyes scanning the river bed keenly, Reece reined his horse up an incline to where Harris was now standing up, searching the arroyo with intense concentration.

The distant thunder of racing hoofs could still be heard as Reece swung down beside Frank and crumpled to the ground. "Damned leg!" he said gruffly.

Harris took off his kerchief and wrapped the torn, bleeding leg. "Bone shot," he said. "You won't be able to ride for a while with that." He stood back then, and fixed Reece with a dark, blazing stare. "Now do you mind tellin' me just what the hell you mean by scatterin' our herd all over the God-damned territory? Take days to find 'em."

Reece groaned with pained fury. "What are you kickin' about? You're still wearin' your hair!"

"I was doin' all right! I could've picked those Indians off one by one as they come around the bend!"

Reece gritted his teeth with indignant fury and hurt. "I wish I'd let you try it!"

Several of the cowboys rode up to them, and Frank said evenly, "Mendoza. Reece got his leg shot up. We'll have to put him in the wagon for a while. Till he mends, I'll take over the herd."

Reece struggled to stand, but could not. "Who d'you think you are? Mendoza takes over!"

His voice still flat, Frank said, "I'm the partner here. Not Mendoza." He turned toward the cowhands. "Doc. You and Slim stay here a bit and watch to see if those Comanches come back along. Though I don't doubt they're havin' a fine time helpin' themselves to the herd by now. Curtis, you and Capper get Reece in the wagon and keep him out of the way.

"We're goin' to work straight through until we get that herd rounded up. Mendoza, we'll want to get every man till back in camp, except for a couple of guards. We're goin' to start chasing those cows back in right now."

Mendoza studied him evenly. "Sí, señor."

"An' don't sí señor me, which means you're bein' polite. An okay'll do."

The Spaniard grinned. "Okay."

Frank stepped into saddle and rode briskly toward camp.

"Wait a minute!" Reece called, too late. Settling back in agony, he grated, "I oughtta tear him in half!"

"Sit still, boss." Mendoza forced him to lie calmly. "Or you'll tear your leg in half." He added with a casual shrug, "He is young yet. Full of beans and vinegar. What can go wrong? I'll keep an eye on things." Turning to Capper, he said, "Cut some splints for the leg."

When the leg was set and splinted, Frank rode up with the rest of the crew in tow. "Ready to go, Mendoza?"

"Yes."

"We'll probably be gone two or three days this first

time out," Frank told Reece. "I'm leaving four men i‹
camp with you. There's a helluva big pile of brush jus‹
outside camp. Comanches give you trouble, light it."

"Sure you won't get lost?" Reece asked.

"One thing I'm sure of. I won't run the herd off o‹
purpose." Mendoza was asaddle beside him now, an‹
Frank said. "Let's go!"

CHAPTER SIXTEEN

Wɪᴛʜ both the toughness and the new authority he'd voted himself, Frank found strength within him he'd never knew existed. He was in the saddle seventy-two hours on that first impossible hunt through the broken country. When they got back to camp with nearly a thousand steers wrangled out of every gully and draw within a hundred square miles, he was the only man in the crew who hadn't got at least ten or twelve hours sleep through the three days. And even then, his mind was alert and his rawhide-tough, lean body was ready to absorb more punishment if need be.

"Gawd!" Charley told Curtis, who had stayed behind with Reece. "We was practically diggin' cows outa prairie dog holes. We lifted every rock and peeked into ev'ry hollow tree in Texas!" He moaned sadly, "It was hard!"

"We'll be going out again at daybreak," Frank said. "Curtis'll be able to find out for himself." Speaking loudly enough for everyone to hear, he added, "We got the easy ones. From now on, the looking will be harder. The man who rounds up the most strays, starting now, gets a hundred-dollar bonus when we hit Chicago."

Frank was the first man up in the morning, and as he passed the wagon where Reece lay, the man spoke through the still, gray shadows. "Good idea, that bonus thing. Makes the men feel better."

"Who cares how they feel? It'll bring in at least another thousand dollars' worth of cows. Plain good business. Besides, you're paying the reward."

After ten days of grueling work; hauling steers out of crevasses, rounding them up out of sandy wastes, mud holes and rocky ground, where every step might break a horse's leg, they'd retrieved better than two thousand

113

head. But the killing pace set by Frank was beginning to tell on the men.

Frank rode into camp one afternoon to find Charley yelling at Curtis.

"Get off my bedroll, Curtis, or I'll break your damn head!"

"Sleep on mine. Ain't laid down since yesterday mornin', and I ain't movin' for nobody!"

"Like hell you ain't!" Charley reached down and grabbed the other man and they wound up rolling across the ground in a threshing mass of kicking legs and striking fists.

"Cut it out!" Frank said.

Neither of them heard him, and Curtis got on top of Charley, at last pinning him with his knees on Charley's shoulders. Taking out a knife, he snarled, "You think that Mex hurt you? Ain't nothin' compared—"

Frank had walked over to them and now he repeated with authority, "Stop it, Curtis."

"Who's gonna make me?" Curtis turned back to Charley.

Frank took out his revolver and slammed the barrel of it across Curtis's wrist and the knife flew to the ground. "I am." He put the gun back in its holster. "You want to try me or you want to try sleeping on your own bedroll?"

Grumbling, rubbing his hurt wrist, Curtis got up and went to his roll to stretch out. Charley got up and dusted himself off. "Thanks, Harris."

"Next time you get in a brawl, it's you I'll damage."

Charley flopped on his bunk and was soon snoring soundly.

From where he sat in a folding chair with his leg propped on a log before him, Reece said, "Come here, Harris."

Standing before him, Frank said, "What you want?"

"Better slack off. Boys are gettin' mean."

"I'll slack off. The roundup's finished as of this afternoon. Only got eight steers today. Not worth while to go on any more."

"How many you figure got lost?"

"Better than three hundred."

Reece shook his head. "A lot of cows."

"Yeah. Too bad. Too bad for you, that is."

"What about you?"

Harris shrugged. "We found all my cows. Turned out all the ones that ran off were yours."

"Oh?" Reece frowned up at Frank. "That's very interesting. How did you go about separating mine from yours?"

"Easy. I used a crowbar."

In the days that followed they moved north again, seeming to inch their way over the vast plains of central Texas, so huge that even the wide, half-mile sprawl of cattle seemed like a tiny ink stain on a desk whenever Frank happened to be chasing strays and viewed the procession from a distant hill.

The biting, driving winds of late fall were on them as they crossed into Kansas and pushed on toward Wichita. Night riding became a bitterly cold task as winter loomed nearer, and the graveyard shift often came in with frost on their eyebrows, blue lips and hands so stiff from cold they could hardly be moved.

As the slow, hard weeks of time and miles of distance fell behind them, Reece improved steadily. He could walk with a crutch by the time they stopped by at the Flying R spread, and in Kansas he finished carving a fancy, scrolled cane out of a solid chunk of oak.

The first day he tried the cane and managed to walk, Mendoza and the others congratulated him happily. Frank simply said, "Hope the experience taught you not to charge into a mob of Comanches again. You were lucky this time."

As Harris walked away, Reece told Mendoza, "The way Bat Masterson got his nickname, he'd been shot in the leg and was walkin' around Dodge with a cane. He batted a couple of smart alecks over the head with the cane one day, and come to be known as Bat." He stared at the retreating figure of Harris. "I am sorely tempted to follow Masterson's shining example."

At noon one unusually warm and sunny day, they came to a railroad track that ran across the Kansas prairie in either direction as far as the eye could see. The cowboys let out cheers of joy, and as they were joking and whooping and bragging about what they intended to do in town, Mendoza said to Frank, "Got it whipped, boss! Wichita's no more'n five miles east along the tracks!"

As they swung the herd at right angles, Doc Bender rode to where Frank was flanking left, between the herd and the tracks. "Harris," he said. "Might as well tell you, and get it over with. I'm going to draw my time when we get into town."

Frank's face clouded with regret, and for a moment he almost forgot to be tough. Then he said evenly, "I'm sorry to hear that, Doc. I think you know pretty well that without you and Mendoza I'd have never got this herd through."

The gunman's serious, kind eyes warmed as he glanced at Frank. "Comin' from you, that's something. It's harder to get a good word outa you than it ever was from Reece."

"It is?" Frank was taken by surprise at this idea.

"Yeah. My own feeling is you're tryin' too hard to be like him."

In Wichita's stockyards, where they milled the herd into pens standing near track sidings, Bender went to Reece. "I'm sorry to be leavin' you, Tom. But I'd like to draw my pay. Gonna hang around Wichita a while."

Reece reached into his pocket to take out a fat roll of bills.

"The crew won't be as good without you." Counting quickly and silently, he said, "I make it six months' salary. Hundred and eighty dollars."

"Closer to five months."

"Close enough to six."

As Doc pocketed the bills, Reece went on, "Thought you were all through with Wichita."

"Well, I figure if I'm not the marshal, maybe I can live here peaceful." Doc spoke slowly. "I got friends here. I like to be with 'em. So there's no harm in tryin'."

"How'd an easygoin' gent like you ever come to be a gunman in the first place?"

Doc grinned sadly. "Kinda snuck up on me." He reached out to shake hands. "So long, Tom. Maybe I'll see you next time through."

"Bye, Doc. Luck."

Their second day in Wichita the news got to them. They were loading the balky, bawling steers into cattle cars and almost had the job wound up. Astride the top rail and armed with a stick, Frank was jabbing the cows up a slanting shoot to the last of twelve cars. "This one's about filled, Mendoza," he called over the stomping and the truculent lowing of the steers. "Better send down for another string."

Mendoza jotted a figure down on a dirty slip of paper in his hand. "I count eighteen hundred loaded. Another string of a dozen cars ought to hold us okay."

Reece was seated outside the pens on a stack of railroad ties, his cane propped beside him. Charley came running between the rows of pens and shouted, "You hear about Doc Bender? He's dead! Killed himself!"

Mendoza and the other cowboys, except for Frank, who stayed astraddle the fence by the chute, gathered around Charley and Reece. "You're crazy or drunk!" Curtis accused Charley. "Or both!"

"Like hell I am!"

"Tell us what you know," Reece said. "If you're jokin', you're fired."

"Honest to God, I'm tellin' the truth!" Charley insisted. "He was in some saloon drinkin' with a couple of friends. Some fellow walks in nobody ever saw before.

Asks Doc if he's Doc Bender who used t' be marshal in town.

"Well, Doc says yes, and the fellow says, 'Then I'm gonna kill you.' He starts to take his gun out as fast as he can, an' Doc shoots him. Kills him!"

"Well, if Doc kilt him, then why in hell is Doc dead?" Curtis demanded.

"That's what I'm tellin' you! Doc didn't say nothin' at all. He puts his gun back, walks outa the saloon, and crosses over to Hanson's livery stable. His friends knew how Doc was—that he was feelin' bad. So after a while they went over to talk to him.

"They found 'im hangin' out back of the stalls! He'd hung himself. He was dead!"

Breathless from his story, Charley stopped, still panting slightly from his long run to the pens.

Curtis said, with shocked confusion, "Doc won his fight fair and square. What'd he wanta go and kill himself for?"

Frank had listened to Charley without moving. His face twisted with sorrow, he dropped off the top rail and out of sight of the others. There were tears in his eyes, and he brushed them aside angrily. "He killed the hawk," he said to himself senselessly. "He saved that silly little rabbit!" Composing his face into firm lines, he walked out from behind the pens. "Well, there's nothing we can do about it," he said. "Let's get to work. We got cattle to load!"

The cowboys moved back to their loading positions, shaking their heads in amazement and arguing the thing back and forth. Mendoza and Reece were both staring at Frank; they had both been hard hit by the news.

Reece made no attempt to conceal his feelings. "You just don't give a damn, do you?" he asked, his voice tight.

"You told me once a man had to be tough. Not just in body, you said, but tough of mind and tough of hide. I'm playin' the rules you taught me!"

Reece's voice was low. "If you had anything inside

worth savin', I'd beat you until I'd knocked it out into the open. But that wouldn't do any good. Because it isn't there. You haven't gotten tough. You've just gotten miserable."

The cowman hopped down from the ties onto his good leg, picked up his cane and limped away.

CHAPTER SEVENTEEN

Rᴇᴇᴄᴇ's special cattle train, rented from the Santa Fe Railroad Company, consisted of a locomotive, forty-six cattle cars, and a caboose that the Flying R crew shared with an engineer and brakeman.

The cowboys spent their time smoking and loafing, talking about the women they knew in Chicago, and playing cards.

Reece was beating Mendoza and three others in a dealer's-choice poker game the last night out of Chicago when Capper opened the trap door in the caboose roof and climbed down the ladder.

Joe took off his gloves and warmed his hands at the potbelly stove. "Boss, them tracks're gettin' awful rough. Slammin' the steers pretty bad."

"We can feel it," Reece told him as the chair he was sitting on bounced under the impact of wheels banging over a track gap below. "Same old story. How many of 'em down?"

"Four down in one car."

"Four?" Reece put his cards down. "Hell, four times forty-six is nearly two hundred!"

"Mosta the cars ain't that bad. I think that one's got square wheels on it."

Frank had been stretched out on a wall bunk. Now he got down, put on his hat and jacket, and climbed out of the caboose.

"Where's he goin'?" Reece wondered aloud. After studying his three-card draw, he threw his cards down. "Pass." Capper drew his gloves on and started back up the swaying ladder, and the cowman said, "Check to see what Harris is up to while you're out there."

A few minutes later, Joe scrambled down the ladder

120

once more. "He's crazy! He's in the car tryin' to heave them four downed steers back onto their feet!"

"He's prob'ly hamburger by now," Curtis said.

Reece stood up and Mendoza said, "Where you going?"

"Deal me out." Reece swung up the ladder, favoring his game leg. He called down, "What car?"

"Number eight."

On top of the caboose, the cold, whipping wind tore at him as he went gingerly along the catwalk of the swaying, bouncing train. His leaps from the top of one car to the next were more of a hop than a jump, for his right leg still had far less than its full strength.

At Number Eight, he climbed down the ladder to the narrow platform at the end. The top part of the stall-like double door was open, and inside the dark car he could see the shadowed figure of a man in the swaying crush of cattle. As he watched, the man grunted in pain as he was trapped against the wall between the forward tipped horns of a big steer.

The walls of the car were separated slats, and Reece crawled in through the top of the door and with toe holds and finger holds in the open channels between the slats he made his way along the wall to where Frank was trapped.

The big steer was not deliberately killing him; it couldn't have moved if it had wanted to. Reece dropped down two steers away and started pushing and twisting the cattle toward a small open space near the center of the car. The creatures stood sprawl-footed and stubborn, leaning against each other and the walls for support sometimes, at other times shifting weight for reasons they alone knew, or even, occasionally, trying to take a walk through or over the others.

When Reece had shoved two other steers out of the way, he had cleared room for the big brute pinning Frank against the wall. He grabbed its horns, twisted them and struck the beast in the nose with his fist at the last mo-

ment, to clear it away quickly before one of the horn
went into Frank.

Gasping for breath, Frank looked at Reece with word
less gratitude, unable to speak. His shirt and jacket had
been ripped by flailing horns, and he was bleeding along
the ribs from a shallow gash.

Searching over the shadowy car, lighted only by dim
star shine and moonlight coming through the slats, Reece
saw that only two steers were down now. Frank had got
the other two to their feet.

"I suppose the two that're down are mine," he said.

After a moment Frank could speak. "Depends whether
we can get 'em up or not." He took a deep breath and
went on. "You shouldn't be in here, with your bum leg."

The swaying train hit an especially wide gap and the
same steer that had trapped Frank, now standing side
ways to them, nearly crushed them both as it leaned onto
them backed by the weaving weight of several neighbors.
"Nobody in their right mind should be down here,"
Reece grunted, shoving the beast away. "But since your
two steers are back on their feet, let's pry my two up off
the floor."

Working as a team through the shifting, swaying, toss
ing press of sheer weight and horns, they forced their
way to the first downed cow. Reece slammed against the
steers slowly trampling the creature to death, budging
them slowly away, and Frank kicked the animal in the
ribs to stir it. The longhorn turned its eyes on Frank and
looked at him with calm indignation. Frank grabbed it
by the nose and ear and hauled up until, complaining
with a throaty bawl, it lurched awkwardly to its feet.

They battled their slow way to the last downed steer.
Getting to it first, Reece reached down and twisted its
tail hard, but it failed to disturb the suicide-bent creature.
He reached forward for the ears, and a waving horn
caught him on the head with crashing force. He went
down and a hoof caught him on the shoulder, then another stomped with blinding pain on his bad leg, as the
steers bawled and shifted position.

Frank was only a few feet behind him, but for a long, horrible moment he might as well have been a mile away. He was caught behind an immovable, bony rump. Finding the way impossibly barred, he instinctively took a deep breath as though he were going under water and forced himself down under the steer. He hunched under the longhorn's belly and came up free on the far side. Then he plunged in between the cattle surrounding Reece, fighting to clear a path.

Over Reece, he reached to a nearby horn with his left hand for whatever support it might give, and bending down, grabbed Reece's shirt, hauling him to a sitting position.

Frank released the horn then, and pulled the cowman to a standing position with both hands. Kicking a crushing cow in the ribs with his knee, he jarred the animal back far enough to lift Reece in his arms. Glowering at the milling, shifting cattle, he said, "You miserable, slab-sided, thick-skulled, God-damned flea bags!"

Reece moved in his arms, and he said, "Your leg gone on you?"

"No. I'm okay. Put me down." It hurt him, but the leg didn't buckle.

"Reece," Frank said, aware that the cowman's leg wasn't in good shape. "Now that I see that downed cow closer, I can see I made a mistake. It's mine. And I don't give a damn about it. Let's get outa here!"

The train whistle screeched suddenly, and the downed cow leaped to its feet, pushing the others out of the way in its fright.

Reece grinned, then surged toward the wall, and Frank followed him through the crushing, bawling steers in the swaying boxcar. They made the wall at last and climbed above the menacing horns. Inching their way along the slatted wall, they finally dropped safely to the platform outside the door at the end of the car.

Wiping sweat from his forehead, Frank saw that his hand was trembling slightly. "Reece," he said. "I never been in a mess like that before. And if I hadn't been

pushing cows around all the way from Mexico, I wouldn'
have been able to get out. Wouldn't have known the wa
cows move, the funny angles they can toss their horns an
kick—that sort of thing."

"Yeah?" Reece said, testing his leg gingerly.

"I guess I know now why you went into that cattl
game down in Chihuahua. And speakin' of cattle, I gues
those weren't all yours that we lost in the stampede. I'd sa
it was more like fifty-fifty."

Reece looked at him levelly on the dark, swaying plat
form. "Seems a fair split. Make a bargain with you. Nex
time outa Wichita, let's leave off wrassling the brute
barehanded that way. It's worse'n that Mexican gam
any time. Let's just get the fellow up front to blow hi
whistle more often."

Frank grinned. "That seems reasonable, Reece."

"Name's Tom."

Tom and Frank surged through the door of the Roya
Hotel on the crest of a small, human stampede of thei
own. Striding to the desk at the head of a herd of well
dressed cattle buyers, dirt-caked cowboys and assorted
party-bent cattlemen, they paused to sign the register

Reece signed in his elaborate, careful scroll, "Reece
Harris & Party," and said, "How are you, Fowler?"

"Ahh, Mr. Reece, it is good to see you again!"

"My partner, Frank Harris, used to be in the hote
business himself, so you'd better take good care of us."

"Of course! As always!" Fowler took a second lool
at the tanned, lean man standing beside Reece. His face
went through a subtle manipulation so that shocked
surprise managed to come out as a genial beam. "Why
you're—or you were, our Mr. Harris! Well, you've come
a long way, sir!"

Frank grinned with easy assurance. "Hello, Fowler."

One of the cattle buyers said, "Reece, price has gone
up some. You're in luck. We can offer you three and
one-quarter cents a pound, free and clear. For every cow
you got."

"Yeah?" Reece shrugged. "What do you think, Frank?"

Frank put an elbow on the hotel desk and tilted his hat back. Looking soberly from Reece to the buyer, he said, "I don't think, Tom, that these gentlemen really appreciate our position. You see, mister, when you take a nice long ride with a bunch of cows the way we do, you get very attached to them. At the end of trail, you sort of feel you know each one of them, kind of personally. And you hate to give them up. Especially at three and one-quarter cents a pound."

"He's right," Reece agreed quietly. "You become downright fond of the animals."

"Your wing is ready Mr. Reece, Mr. Harris," Fowler said, "and the ballroom. Is there anything you want sent up?"

"Yeah," Reece called over his shoulder. "Thirty or forty chickens. Couple cases of whisky. Stuff to get us started. And we want plenty of hot water!"

As the crowd of men thronged up the staircase, they flanked left to allow a young woman with soft red hair to pass.

Frank's eyes followed the young woman with open appreciation, and Reece said, "Matter of fact, I had a hunch you'd like redheads. Took the liberty of lining one up for you. To take to the opera tonight. If you'll come."

"Never been to an opera. Might as well try it once." Frank glanced at Reece. "How'd you know I like redheads?"

"Easiest thing in the world," Reece shrugged. "Any man likes redheads."

THE END
of a Gold Medal Original by
CLAIR HUFFAKER

No doubt about it—Gold Medal Westerns are the best!

In the Critics' Western Ratings Chart, Gold Medal Westerns placed the first five books listed, and in the complete list of thirteen books, seven were Gold Medal's.

Read these new Gold Medal Westerns!

S661. MARICOPA TRAIL by *Noel Loomis*

679. GUN TALK AT YUMA by *Frank Castle*

686. LAST STAND AT PAPAGO WELLS by *Louis L'Amour*

692. HANG THE MEN HIGH by *Noel Loomis* and *Paul Leslie Peil*

631. VIOLENCE VALLEY by *William Heuman.*

656. WESTWARD THE DRUMS by *L. A. Hearne*

696. APACHE RISING by *Marvin H. Albert*

25c-EXCITING WESTERN NOVELS-25c

We'll be glad to send any of these never-before-published Gold Medal Books to you direct by mail. Simply follow the directions at the end of this list.

692. HANG THE MEN HIGH
Noel Loomis and *Paul Leslie Peil*
He was called the Hanging Judge, and he was rightly named. The gallows held twelve nooses; the deputies had twelve killers in the county jail. "We'll hang them all at once," the judge declared, "then we'll look for more."

696. APACHE RISING *Marvin H. Albert*
The Apaches had left the reservation. Their faces were daubed with war paint and somehow they had found rifles. Men, women and children were being slaughtered and scalped—tortured as only the Apaches knew how to do it. Someone had to stop them!

699. COMANCHE VENGEANCE *Richard Jessup*
Sarah was a woman with a mission—to find the Indian who had tortured her husband to death, scalped her baby son and raped her small daughter. She rode into Indian Territory and Duke followed her. A guardian angel, he was—with a fast gun.

700. THE TALL STRANGER *Louis L'Amour*
The tall stranger came out of nowhere and saved them. He was a rangy man, with the West in his walk and lightning in his draw. The people on the wagon train feared him almost as much as the Indians he had saved them from.

705. STAGECOACH WEST *William Heuman*
They offered to let him ride gun on the stagecoach carrying $40,000 in gold. He took the job—because he was too proud to say no.

706. MASSACRE AT SAN PABLO *Lewis B. Patten*
No one was left but Mark. He saddled his horse and set out on the trail of the scalpers. They were white men, he knew. He would see to it that they died as slowly and painfully as his family and friends had.

713. SUMMONS TO SILVERHORN *Kenneth Fowler*

The summons came from Blaine's father: find the ma[n] who shot your brother in the back. Blaine had to retur[n] to the town he hated and the town that hated him; to th[e] father who had never wanted him; to the woman wh[o] had laughed at him.

714. AMBUSH ON THE MESA *Gordon D. Shirreffs*

A regiment was needed but they sent only one man— Hugh Kinzie, scout for the United States Army. Kinzie['s] orders were to save the party of men and women fro[m] ambush by the raging Apaches.

720. BARREN LAND SHOWDOWN *Luke Short*

A hard-hitting story of the West—where men's temper[s] flared too easily, where the whole Territory wasn't larg[e] enough to hold the two men who had sworn to get eac[h] other.

722. A TOWN TO TAME *Joseph Chadwick*

He was a tough-looking man with a law badge pinned t[o] his shirt. It was up to him to bring law to a lawless tow[n] and he was frightened. Frightened because the magi[c] had gone from his gun hand, because his draw wasn['t] fast enough any more.

723. FIVE RODE WEST *Lewis B. Patten*

Five of them started out—but how many would retur[n] from the suicidal mission? The herd they had to reac[h] would have to be smuggled out of the Territory unde[r] the guns of Indians and outlaws.

728. HELLER WITH A GUN *Louis L'Amour*

From the man who gave you HONDO comes this blazing new tale of King Mabry, the quiet man born to violence bred to wildness, who walked in the shadow of his ow[n] death-dealing hand!

733. GUNS OF RIO CONCHOS *Clair Huffaker*

From behind their stolen guns, the Comanches screame[d] defiance. And there was only one man to stop them— Riot Holliday, a man with hate in his heart and six months to live.

If your local dealer cannot supply you, send 25 cents for eac[h] copy desired, plus 5 cents per book for handling and mailing, to **GOLD MEDAL BOOKS, FAWCETT PUBLICATIONS, INC., GREENWICH, CONN.** *Please order by number and title. Canadian orders cannot be accepted.*